Feeling The Rainbow

A
BODY
INNOCENT
The true story
of one woman's spiral
into the depths of
manic-depressive
illness

Donna Dobrenchuk Noble
WITH
RICHARD MITCHENER

Published by Sound Health Enterprises
115 Spruce Street, Aurora, Ontario L4G 3T5

Cover art by David Noble
Page make-up by Kennedy (DTP) Productions

Printed and manufactured in Canada by Trio Printing Inc.

DEDICATION

Feeling the Rainbow was written with feelings, faith and love and it is dedicated in memoriam to a very special lady, my mom. She taught me that to give of oneself is the greatest joy. This book is also dedicated to the many hurting people who have shared their feelings, enabling me to grow and to begin to learn to fly, freely, without restrictions or bounds.

It's been fourteen months since I first sat at the dining room table with Donna Noble. Mugs of steaming coffee before us, she took a deep breath and began to unfold the outlines of an incredible story, her story, and that of the relatives, friends and acquaintances who had entered her circle over the course of time. As she spoke, I couldn't believe that this woman—beautiful, vibrant, elegant, articulate, with rock-solid reason and particularly remarkable insight to herself and others—could have gone through such experiences.

Hers was a story of the slow decline into the depths of serious mental illness, of the seemingly innocuous events that, woven together imperceptibly over time, compounded themselves into subtle causes of manic-depressive illness. Eventually, for reasons no one fully understands, tiny molecules—chemicals—in her brain underwent a small change, invisibly, secretly, and Donna went off the deep end, as they say, into a world of another rationality, of other perspectives.

I wasn't a stranger to manic-depressive illness. Years ago, to earn enough to enter a doctoral program, I found work in a new city and temporarily rented a room in a house owned by a woman in her late fifties. Her name was Agnes. After some time, in conversation she revealed that she had had a history of manic-depressive illness, with six separate experiences in the state mental institution. Her treatment, the standard medicology of the time, clearly had been inadequate: on some evenings, tucked away in my little corner room, I actually feared for my life. For most of my time there, Agnes's behavior could be described only as bizarre, and after three months I moved to a house that was much closer to work and considerably saner.

Today, after untold gallons of coffee and months of grinding out the details of this account with Donna, I'm certain that she is as absolutely rational—sane? mentally sound?—as anyone could possibly be. Given the nature of the mental illness she'd experienced, was this obvious "normalcy" the product of the "standard medicology" that Agnes—and so many others—had received? As the narrative continues, I find the answer to be 'no.' Such results came largely from other sources, the revelation of which awaits completion of a subsequent chapter.

In kindness, however, we offer a clue from Shakespeare's *Macbeth*, Act V, Scene 3:

> <u>Macbeth</u>:   Cure her of that:
> Canst thou not minister to a mind diseased,
> Pluck from the memory a rooted sorrow,
> Raze out the written troubles of the brain,
> And with some sweet oblivious antidote
> Cleanse the stuft bosom of that perilous stuff
> Which weighs upon the heart?
> <u>Doctor</u>: Therein the patient must minister to himself.
> <u>Macbeth</u>: Throw physic to the dogs—I'll none of it.

Richard B. Mitchener
Willowdale, Ontario
19 March 1988

PREFACE

Each of us comes into this world a fresh and resilient creation, with a nervous system much like a new rubber band, loaded with elasticity to withstand much stretching and pulling. But as each day brings the wear and tear of stress and problems, that elasticity can weaken. Unlike the simple rubber band, we humans have a complex nervous system that must bear the feelings as well as the actions of being stretched and yanked and twisted in our daily lives.

Doctors tell us that each of us has a weak link, or Achilles' heel, which can be affected by too much negative stress. Thus the difficulty begins here if you happen to be born with a genetic sensitivity toward depressive illness, like myself. I seem to have inherited a double dose, since depressive illness has occurred on both sides of my family. But somehow I found little comfort in this fact when a doctor, trying to explain my diagnosis, commented, "Oh, don't worry. Of all the mental illnesses, you have the best one. And besides, all Ukrainians have depressive illness anyway."

I could never understand the childhood statement, "Sticks and stones may break my bones, but names will never hurt me." We're all hurt by words and names and labels. Even though the outward body shows no scars or bruises, the inside band of feelings and emotions may be nicked and chipped away with hundreds of emotional wounds. Psychologists estimate that for every physical illness, we may suffer as many as sixty emotional hurts that wear down the body's resistance, that can eventually bring about pain and even cripple. All of us must endure pain and suffering in our lifetimes, but some seem to feel more intensely than others, or at least recover from the hurts at a much slower rate. Others seem to tolerate enormous pain and yet appear unscathed. I have always been fascinated with feelings. Why are we all made so differently in this way? Why are feelings so important? I write this book in the hope of shedding some light on the fact that feelings can and do have a very definite effect on our health.

Mandy Cartwright Marsden is a character of my imagination, but the story is true, describing in part an autobiographical sketch of my own battle to overcome manic-depressive illness, which appeared fully nine years ago. Mandy's description, her life and her experiences could be those of someone very "normal" whom you may know. But there is a slight difference—her elastic band became so frayed that she became mentally ill. Mandy appears as a young woman in the story, but she really expresses the thoughts and actions of several men and women who have until now suffered in silence, perhaps too afraid to recognize that their grief and pain need not be.

This book and the two that follow (because *Feeling the Rainbow* is actually three volumes) will seek to show that people suffering emotional illness can rise above the stigma and label of being "mental patients in a medical mold." It is my attempt to show instead that we are simply hurting people who happen to be stuck in varying degrees of crisis, with little or no awareness of how to get out.

As founder of several self-help groups for depression and manic depression in Canada over the past five years, I have come to know that, although manic-depressive illness has been classified as a biochemical disorder of the brain that can be controlled with medication, hundreds of people's stories I have heard lead me to believe there is much more to the illness still to be understood.

Everyone is in agreement that the illness is very difficult to treat because there seems to be no single cause. Consequently, specialists are constantly arguing about the best modes of treatment, be it therapy, medication or a combination of the two. *Feeling the Rainbow: A Body Innocent* allows us to see the process of evolving illness from a patient's perspective. It is not meant to be a how-to manual of treatment of a clinical case study. I chose a novel format because Mandy didn't just wake up one day the victim of mental illness; it doesn't just strike without warning. But the signs and symptoms are sometimes subtle, almost innocent, and they accumulate as we continue to ignore unresolved negative stresses that we encounter along the path of life. I leave it to you to see how many you can identify in the story.

Feeling the Rainbow doesn't claim to have all the answers. It's my hope to stimulate you to ask questions and seek to find out more about how damaging unresolved emotion can be to our physical well-being.

I see now that my background in physical education and health has been invaluable in preparing me to understand in such detail the physical components of my illness. That background gave me a head start in writing this book. But I thank Richard Mitchener for his technical assistance in enabling me to best express my thoughts and ideas on paper, for I never professed to be a writer, just the creator of this story. Our combined knowledge and love of New England allowed for some favorite places in our memories to stay real: such places as Falmouth Heights, Farmington, Freeport, Mount Katahdin, Filene's Basement, L.L. Bean's and Durgin Park really do exist. But similarities between other characters, businesses and places described in Mandy's life and real people, firms or places is coincidental and unintentional.

Hebrews 11:34 reads, "out of your weakness shall come strength." God is continually blessing me with talents and abilities that I never dreamed possible nine years ago. And it's very comforting and exciting to learn that psychiatrists are just beginning to study more closely the correlation between depressive illness and creativity. We all have so much yet to learn, and that is what's so exciting to me and what continues to give me hope. Consider the agile cricket that laughs at the ungainly caterpillar, tediously wearing` its cocoon, who announces in a soft voice that soon it will fly to the heavens. All we need do is spread our wings and try.

Donna Dobrenchuk Noble
Aurora, Ontario.

There was a time when meadow, grove, and stream,
The earth, and every common sight,
       To me did seem
       Apparelled in celestial light,
The glory and the freshness of a dream.

It is not now as it hath been of yore; —
       Turn wheresoe'er I may,
       By night or day,
The things which I have seen I now can see no more.

       The rainbow comes and goes,
       And lovely is the rose,
       The moon doth with delight
Look around her when the heavens are bare,
       Waters on a starry night
       Are beautiful and fair;
  The sunshine is a glorious birth:
  But yet I know, where'er I go,
That there hath passed away a glory from the earth.

                    William Wordsworth
          Ode, Intimations of Immortality (1807)

Chapter One

Mandy threw her arms over her head and arched her back in a lazy, wonderfully luxurious stretch. Her eyes still closed, she smiled as she remembered this was her first day free of schedule. It was Friday, but school was officially finished for the seniors; summer vacation had begun. The year was 1963.

The music alarm had been playing for over an hour now. She had drifted in and out of sleep five or six times as the rude harshness of one song and then another would grate over the low volume to wake her. She stirred slightly and through the covers felt something against her leg. As her eyes squinted open and adjusted to the light, she saw the box on the corner of the bed with the cap and gown, neatly folded and packed.

The past two weeks had been full of events Mandy knew she'd never forget. The prom, the class party, the wonderful graduation ceremony last night, the craziness of driving around all last night with David, Shaun and Ellen—so many mixed emotions. She had looked forward to graduation for such a long time, and now it was over. Too suddenly, it seemed.

Mandy brightened. Her job as tennis instructor at the club began next week. And in three short weeks Julie would be coming to spend most of July with her grandparents. The two girls had been especially close, inseparable partners. It had been a year and a half now since Julie's family moved from Massachusetts. During Christmas week six months ago, her family went up to Boston to visit relatives, and Julie's older sister had driven her down to Falmouth for half a day together with Mandy. Except for that time, the two girls hadn't been face to face.

Mandy glanced over at the clock. Eleven-thirty! Mom must have warned Bratley not to wake her before she left for work. Mandy stretched again, arms out and legs pulled up, then she threw the covers off. The box at the foot of the bed fell to the floor. She got up, walked around and reached to pick it up, remembering she had to return it this afternoon.

She looked at the black graduation gown, then picked it up and went to stand in front of the mirror. Her reflection revealed a taut and well-shaped athletic body through the sheer nighty, with firm, nicely rounded breasts, lean waist and muscular thighs. Mandy saw only a disappointing reflection. She slipped the gown over her nighty and reached for the cap. The gown rested well on her shoulders, and for once she was glad to be rather tall. She adjusted the tassel and tried to remember which side meant she'd graduated. How peculiar she felt, almost as if she were standing outside herself. She didn't feel like a graduate, but more like a frightened little girl. Who was this person facing her in the mirror? Why did she feel so different at times, as if she didn't belong here? She remembered asking her mother on several occasions, "Did anything strange happen when I was born?" Once her mom told her it had been a difficult delivery; the forceps had slipped and left an ugly scar on the back of her head. But her hair had always covered that. Otherwise, her mother jokingly reassured her, she hadn't been dropped on her head or anything like that. But Mandy was self-conscious enough not to be quite convinced by mom's explanation. She often felt that her folks were hiding something. And she had always wondered from time to time about her birth. Her vivid imagination often carried her away, and she would pretend she'd had a twin who'd died at their birth, and that was probably why she felt this longing or strange sadness at times.

Mandy drifted back to herself as she took off the cap and gown and tossed back her reddish-blonde hair. It was shoulder length now. Maybe she should have it cut. You need a change, she mused; you look so plain. She pushed her hair up from behind and tipped her head slightly to the side, making a little grimace, unsatisfied with the look. As she did, the odd little dimple at the corner of her cheekbone—the other reminder of that forceps delivery—showed in the reflection. She felt so awkward standing there. "Why don't my boobs grow?" she demanded angrily to no one in particular. Mandy wasn't comfortable with the way her ribs stuck out, appearing to de-emphasize the size of her breasts. How come I was the first in my class to wear a bra, and

2

then I stopped short? Her hands reached down to encircle her waist, and she wished she had a tiny middle instead of this muscular waist and rather large hips. Nothing looked quite right.

She felt confused. This should be the happiest time in her life. Then why did she seem so restless and unsure? Listening to the graduation speeches last night had even made her weep. Why? "The world is yours; go out and conquer it," they'd said. But she'd had trouble fitting the ideals and hopes and dreams that the speakers encouraged into her view of the future. As much as she'd tried to decide, she just didn't know what to do from here. Even graduating with honors or being class vice-president didn't seem to encourage her. She didn't believe she'd done anything outstanding. Mandy's parents had been so proud, and the beautiful strand of pearls and the sewing machine they'd given her for graduation made her cry. Somehow she didn't feel worthy. She felt like such a fake sometimes.

Life from this point on seemed so vague, so complicated. She'd been in such a hurry to grow up, and now she wasn't ready. "Oh, quit being so serious," she said out loud. It'll get better; you're thinking too deeply. She made a funny little face to herself in the mirror, trying to smile. Her grandmother always used to say, "Smile and the world smiles with you." Too bad you're not here now, Mandy reflected. Gramma had died two years ago, and Mandy wondered then why it's always the good people who seemed to die sooner than they should. That's what confused her about "God's plan for our lives," something she'd heard in her childhood Sunday school classes. Why didn't He take all the miserable old goats first? A frown formed on her face and she suddenly noticed how ugly it looked. She was startled out of her daydream.

"Oh my gosh! I've been standing here looking at myself for almost an hour," she said. She folded the gown and placed it and the silly cap neatly in the box, then ran to the shower. So much for pomp and circumstance.

After a quick cheese sandwich with half a glass of milk, Mandy reached for her purse and keys and went out into the warm day. I love this little town, she thought as she breathed in the slightly salt air lazing in from Nantucket Sound. She walked out to her yellow VW Beetle at the curb, mother's old hand-me-down. She got in, rolled down the window, whispered "Please" as the motor cranked, and breathed a sigh of thanks as it caught. Then she headed off toward the clothing store first, and afterward, she'd swing over to the country club at Falmouth Heights.

The Tecumseh Country Club was an elegant old golf and tennis complex whose white clapboards everywhere were beginning to peel from age and the slow ravage of salt air. The main clubhouse sat imposingly on a rise of the low bluff overlooking the Sound and, five miles offshore, Martha's Vineyard. Somehow, the road that passed between the buildings and the bluff diminished the club's exclusiveness, since this allowed the common masses to drive past the clubhouse. This exposure to the common people always irked the older member families, especially those from Boston who spent their summers here on the Cape. Tecumseh had its share of New England snobbery.

Mandy drove up the graveled approach to the clubhouse and around back to the parking area. She stopped the car and glanced at the tennis courts. On the nearest were two overweight couples dressed in white and wearing white caps with oversized visors; they were hitting balls in every direction but the right one. Beyond them and filling most of the other courts were young, already well-tanned players in their twenties and early thirties. Mandy recognized no one among them; they must be out-of-town members, who usually spent only their summers on the Cape. She watched for a moment and was suddenly shocked to notice how very confident they all appeared. She had to admire the strength of their serves, the certainty of their movements. They were evidently having fun, but clearly they meant business. These were no novice tennis players, she decided. She began to feel unsure of her own ability, though she was among the best on her high school team. I'm glad I'm going to be teaching the kids, she concluded.

To the left of the tennis courts she saw the old golf clubhouse, also in need of paint, where it sat a few hundred feet behind the main house. The golf course itself, with its putting green and the first tee a few paces from the clubhouse porch, sprawled away toward the south, parallel to the road. The course even crossed the road in two places, where club members took their lives in their hands to cross against the tourist traffic to the seventh, where the green hung precipitously over the bluff, and back over between the ninth green and the tenth tee.

Mandy would be a part-time tennis instructor for the summer, teaching juniors from six to twelve years old every day but Sunday. Fortunately, her hours were from nine in the morning to noon, which left her afternoons and evenings free for herself and her friends. It seemed like a good job; it was something she liked and she could save something for college.

Mandy pulled open the back door of the supply room and saw a blonde-haired man in his middle twenties hunched over a box.

"Hi. Can you tell me where I can find Rob McPherson?" she said as he looked up.

"I'm Rob," he grinned, showing off his teeth. "What can I do to you?"

She was immediately put off, and had to fight a blush that instantly came to her face. She therefore decided to dislike this young man. "I'm Mandy Cartwright," she said coldly. "I was supposed to see you about my job with the juniors."

"Hey, I'm sorry," he said, noticing her discomfort. "I thought you were the girl I was supposed to give a lesson to this afternoon. Come on, I'll show you your locker and where the equipment is."

Rob showed her around the clubhouse and pointed out the things she'd have to know. Then they went into the store, where he picked up a white T-shirt with the name "Tecumseh Country Club" emblazoned over the profile of a headdressed Indian with two crossed tennis rackets beneath.

"It'll probably shrink, so you better take a medium, or even a large," he said, smiling.

"Thanks. Should I wear this with shorts or do they prefer skirts?" she asked.

"Shorts or skirt," he said. "Or neither. Some of the oldtimers might have a heart attack, but I wouldn't mind." He flashed his grin. Mandy averted her eyes as she tried to ignore that. She'd have to watch out for Rob; this could be a long summer.

"Hey, I'm sure glad you're doing the brats," Rob added

quickly, again sensing her displeasure. "I lost my cool a couple of times last summer. Hope you do better. By the way, be nice to the kids. Some of the parents can get pretty uppity."

"Thanks for the tip," Mandy replied. "Well, I'd better go. See you Monday."

T-shirt in hand and excited at the prospect of developing her own program for the youngsters, Mandy bounced out of the door, looked over at the courts and smiled to herself. For the first time in her life, Mandy felt really confident about something, in control—except, perhaps, for Rob. Thank God he'd be busy with private lessons. But then, she remembered, tennis was her love, and it was easy to teach what you love. This sure beats waitressing, she thought.

Anne brought a steaming bowl to the kitchen table and set it down in front of Ralph. Brad pretended to stick out his foot as Mandy pulled out her chair to sit down. She glowered at him. "Don't you dare," she threatened.

"Did you get your graduation robe back to the store okay?" Ralph asked as he ladled out a steaming bowl of beef stew and handed it to Mandy.

"Yup. Thanks. It's a gown, Dad, not a robe. Pass the bread and butter please, Brad."

Anne sat down. "How was the club?" she asked.

"I think it's going to be fun," Mandy replied. "I really appreciate it, Dad."

"I'll tell Dan you're pleased," Ralph said. Dan McClintock was on the board of the country club and one of Ralph's friends in Rotary; that connection, in fact, was responsible for Mandy's new job.

Brad, a young fourteen, a bit envious of his older sister and prone to tease her, said, "Now if you can only last more than a week."

"Would you please clam up, Bratley?" Mandy retorted.

"Knock it off, you two," enjoined Ralph. "Can't you enjoy your mother's stew without bickering?"

"Your father's right," said Anne. "Mandy honey, are you going out with David tonight?"

"I guess so. He's going to pick me up about seven-thirty and we're supposed to meet everybody down at the beach."

"Well then, let's finish up and get to the dishes," Anne suggested. "Oh, and let me wrap a couple of those brownies for David. And by the way, dear, I know graduation comes once, but you do have all summer to celebrate. Try not to make it a late night tonight, okay?"

"I won't," said Mandy. "I feel a little funny anyway, a little tired for some reason. We won't be late."

David Slone had been Mandy's boyfriend for three years, ever since the start of their second year of high school. He was quite tall and slim, with a kind face and dark brown hair. Like Mandy, David wasn't particularly serious about life, about the future. Their plans seldom went beyond a few weeks at most. Life was basically here and now, or at best focused on the upcoming weekend. This was largely because they assumed any social event would involve them both. No one had to plan far ahead when a date was assured. Neither ever even considered going out with some other person, and no one thought to ask either of them. Everyone knew they were going steady.

David had worked for four years at his father's grocery store in Falmouth—Warren's Groceries. He spent three hours a day at the store during the school week and eight hours on Saturdays until the summer, when he worked full time for six weeks. Then there would be a two- or three-week vacation before school started again. This pattern gave him a sense of responsibility and a certain maturity beyond that of his peers, not to mention enough pocket money to allow him a substantial savings account and a two-year-old Chevrolet Impala. It also gave him a sense of security such that he never had to consider the future. Why should he worry about choices? His father had already told him of his plan to change the store name this summer to Warren and Son's. All David had to do was say the word.

As much as anything about David, Mandy liked his even temperament and his self-assurance. And he made her laugh. She needed the security that David represented and found comfort in "belonging" to such a person.

Sex for David and Mandy amounted at first to a series of fumbling but pleasurable experimentations, largely kissing and touching, which they both enjoyed immensely. Mandy would have

7

been satisfied with that, but as time went on David became more and more frustrated with just kissing and petting. Eventually, a year and a half into their relationship, they tried intercourse, which for Mandy turned out to be a marvelous mix of pain and pleasure, and for David, the entire meaning of life. Her private joy at now being "a woman," however, was soon overcome by the realization that they hadn't taken any precaution. For two weeks she lived in constant fear that she was pregnant, and prayed earnestly for her period. Shortly afterward, when her period finally arrived, a very relieved Mandy insisted that henceforth David must use a rubber. Of course, he objected heartily:

"I can't feel anything with those things. It's like taking a shower in a raincoat! It takes all the fun out of it. And what happens when I go to the drug store to buy them? Somebody's gonna tell my father for sure."

"I'm sorry," Mandy sympathized. "But I can't get pregnant. You know that as well as I do."

David grudgingly had to agree, and though he was disappointed, he reconciled himself to the situation. Neither, in fact, appreciated the loss of the exquisite sensation they had enjoyed on the first occasion. After a few times with the rubbers, both of them realized that intercourse wasn't all it was cracked up to be—at least when you had to wear a raincoat. In those days before the pill, their solution was therefore to reluctantly make a pact to try to refrain from intercourse, which put stops, self-imposed limitations, on their natural instincts. But David loved her and he went along with her wishes. They had established something of a comfort zone within which they could express their physical love. That part was nice, Mandy knew, but something in her mind was troubling about having sex. Last November something had happened to her at school—something terrible that no one knew about, not even David—something that remained unresolved, that almost spoiled their physical times together, though David was oblivious to Mandy's thoughts.

David pulled into the driveway just at seven-thirty. Mandy yelled, "Bye, Mom, Dad!" and skipped down the porch stairs. David reached over and pushed her door open. "Hi, babe," he said as she got in.

"Hi, lover." She leaned over and gave him a quick kiss, then decided to slide over next to him. "Mom made some more brownies. Here." She handed him the paper bag.

"Hey, thanks. She's really okay. How did it go at the club today?"

"Fine," Mandy said. "It'll take getting used to, but I'll manage." She decided it was best not to mention Rob's crude comments. David put the Impala into drive and they headed for town and Warren's Groceries.

"Where are we going first?" she asked.

"We have to get some hamburger and briquettes, then pick up Steve and Marge. He's got his father's split-drum barbecue for tonight. We're just going to leave it on the beach, and he'll pick it up in the truck in the morning. No one will want to steal it. You didn't have dinner, did you?"

"Sure I did. You didn't say we were going to have dinner." She looked at him crossly.

"Just hamburgers and hot dogs. I thought you knew. Anyway, by the time the coals are ready you'll probably be hungry again."

"I doubt it."

David swung the car into Warren's parking lot, jogged in and grabbed a large package of hamburger, some buns and two bags of coals. "Put this on my account, Tom. See you tomorrow," he called to the clerk. Tom smiled and waved him away.

They drove the few blocks to Marge's house and then to the Heights to pick up Steve and his barbecue. They went past the boats in the harbor, rounded the curve where the road began to parallel the beach, drove up on top of the bluff and past the country club and continued a mile or two beyond to the beach area. A little after eight o'clock they pulled up to the sand dune and parked the car. David and Steve wrested the load up and over the low dune between hummocks of wispy grass and over the boarded walkway down to the beach. Some eight or ten others had already arrived.

They had chosen a spot up near the foot of the dune. Large whitened drift logs rested almost parallel to the shoreline where winter storm waves had tossed them years ago. One log had been turned to form a V with another, providing something of a low enclosure and just the right setting for a group to lean against and carry on conversation. Bits of black, dried seaweed, pieces of shells and the odd seagull feather lay scattered, almost hidden by the still warm white sand. Several of the boys were trying to lug a big piece of driftwood over to a six-foot circle of rocks, just beyond the mouth of the V, for the bonfire. Others were gathering smaller pieces of wood to supplement the kindling someone had brought in a cardboard box.

Steve unfolded the cross-membered stand for the barbecue, then decided they didn't need it. "Let's just rest the thing on the sand," he said. "It won't tip over. Let's just pile sand up around the bottom." Which they did. David then dumped in a whole bag of coals, poured on half a can of fluid, placed the grate on top of the half-drum, and tossed a burning match in. Black smoke curled upward, and one of the boys asked, "Who's got a beer?"

Three good-sized coolers sat on the sand with soft drinks on top. Under them, beneath a shielding of ice, thirty-six cans of beer cooled nicely. This would be a mellow evening if everyone acted discreetly. "Shit, Marge, you forgot the marshmallows," someone complained.

"That's okay," rejoined someone else. "You can roast your weiner over the coals."

General laughter erupted.

Mandy quickly took off her jeans and sweatshirt and adjusted the strap on her swimsuit. "Let's go swimming, David," she said brightly. He threw off his shirt and lifted a leg to remove his pants when she gave him a shove, and he went down. Laughing, Mandy ran lightly toward the waves, turning to see David bearing down on her. With a squeal of mock terror she threw her arms up as he tackled her playfully on the sand. They tumbled together in the sand till he pinned her down. He lay almost on top of her, and they could feel each other's heart racing, and the heat of their bodies.

By now Mandy was too comfortable to struggle. She looked up into his eyes and sighed. As he bent his head to kiss her, they heard the faint applause and catcalls from the group back at the fire. They remained coupled in spite of the audience, kissing and stroking until Mandy felt David growing hard. His full weight now caused extra pressure on her chest and back. With a low moan he repositioned himself in the softness between her legs and moved his hips against hers. His tongue slipped between her lips to coax her mouth open wider, as if to signal how much he wanted her. She wanted him inside her, terribly so, but instead she jerked her shoulders and turned her head to catch her breath. "Hey, we forgot our swim," she said weakly.

David knew what she was saying. He rolled over, stretched out on the sand and stared at the darkening sky, his hands clasped behind his head. Mandy knew she'd spoiled the mood and felt awful. "I'm sorry, David," she whispered, but somehow that didn't seem to matter to him. He didn't seem to hear. She'd read that you weren't supposed to stop in the middle of lovemaking and she hoped she'd stopped things in time, before she hurt him. But she was too afraid or shy even to ask.

"Well, hell, let's get wet. I could use a cold shower anyway," David muttered. She ran before him toward the water. He had started to walk, but as he got closer to the water he picked up speed and went crashing through the surf and dove into a wave about to break. After a few moments of romping and splashing each other, they embraced in the waist-deep water and kissed warmly, bodies close against each other. There was something very sensual about kissing while you were almost naked and soaking wet. Reluctantly, Mandy moved away from David, realizing that this would just make him more frustrated. She squeezed his hands and said, "Come on, let's go dry off." Each with an arm around the other, they turned and walked out onto the sand and back to the warmth of the fire.

The sunset behind the group went unnoticed, as there were virtually no clouds, and a chill crept down over the dune. The few others who had gone in for a swim now dried off and covered up. Sweaters and jackets came on and more wood went onto the bonfire. After last night's graduation activities and the parties, most of the sixteen or so people here were subdued, quiet. Against the steady rhythm of waves breaking in the shallow water, only the sound of low rock music from a transistor radio and an occasional loud bellow hinted of a party gathering.

David sat with his arm draped over Mandy's shoulder; they leaned against a log that lay a short distance from the group. They stared out toward Nantucket Island, east of Martha's Vineyard and just visible in the dusk. "It's funny," Mandy said. "All the years I've lived here, I've been to Martha's three or four times, but I've never gone out there."

"There's not much difference between them," said David. "A lot of rich houses and stuff, an airport. The only difference I've seen is the whaling museum. Martha's doesn't have one of those."

Dim lights from Nantucket flickered across the distance in the closing darkness. "The world's just so big, and I haven't been anywhere," Mandy went on, caught up in the moment. "There's so much out there to see. And I haven't even been to Nantucket."

"Well, hell then, we'll just have to take a ride out there some day," he said expansively, but without committing himself.

Mandy's thoughts floated back to the beach, to her best friend, who would be arriving soon for a long-awaited visit.

"Ummh, by the way, David, Julie's going to need someone to go out with when she comes. Who can we get for her?"

"Oh, I don't know. Maybe Pete Michaelson. He's been to Philadelphia, and he knows her. Or that smart guy, Brian, in your biology lab. There are lots of guys that would want to go out with her. She's a good-looking broad."

"Pete would be good," Mandy said. "Why don't you call him and ask? Remind him that Julie's pretty and lots of fun and all that. And we've got to arrange for lots of fun things to do. Maybe we could go around to Woods Hole and see the new changes they've made. We could even drive over to Newport for the jazz festival. I'll have to plan lots of different things to choose from. I can't wait. We've got so much to catch up on."

David looked at Mandy's profile and hesitated. Then he said, "You'll be starting at the club on Monday..."

"Yes, I'm really excited about it."

"I suppose you are." He spoke sullenly.

Mandy sensed that he was troubled. "What's the matter?" she asked.

"Nothing."

"No, what is it?"

He paused, irritated. He took a long slug of beer. After a few moments he admitted, a bit truculently, "It's just that you'll be over there with those rich buggers. I didn't think I'd mind, but I do."

"Oh, David, it's just a summer job, and it's only part-time. I don't care for them any more than you do. The only thing that can happen is that my game will improve. And before we know it, summer will be over anyway."

"That's another thing," he said. He swept his hand toward the group, most of whom were huddled around the bonfire, talking and drinking. "Half of these guys won't be here in the fall. We haven't even talked about us, with you going to Farmington."

David looked into Mandy's eyes, and she thought she saw fear in his.

She hugged her knees against the evening chill. "I don't know," she said. "I still don't like the idea of being apart from you, leaving Falmouth. My dad's been planning and saving for years for me to go to college. I love you, Dave, but you know we can't get married yet, and there's not much work around here. I simply can't disappoint my parents."

She leaned her head on his shoulder, and his arm tightened around her.

They were quiet for a few moments, each realizing for the first time that their paths would diverge, each feeling something like a brick in the pit of the stomach.

"Well, hell," David said. "I'm really bushed from last night. How about you?"

"I can hardly keep my eyes open." She brought her watch close to her face and squinted.

"Do you know it's only ten-thirty? Guess this past week or two has finally caught up with us."

"This'll be a record for an early Friday night, but maybe we'd better take off anyway," David suggested. He helped her up and they walked slowly over to the fire, now low and intimate. Only three hardy couples remained, and one of the boys was softly strumming a guitar.

"Where is everybody?" asked David.

Shaun said, "They took off. Steve and Marge got a ride in already. We're going to crack one or two more beers before we hit the road. Can't let them go to waste."

"We're tired," said Mandy, trying to smile. "We'll see you guys later. Ellen, you keep your eye on Shaun's driving. 'Nite."

They turned toward the dune and the darkness.

In the car David turned on the motor and let it warm up at a low idle. He poked the radio on, then reached over and put his arm around Mandy, who leaned into his kiss. David moved his head back, looked at her closely and said, "I love you, babe."

"I love you too."

He reached for her breast under her jacket and gently smoothed the material of her blouse over her contours. He undid a button, slid his hand under her bra and moved his fingers over her nipple. He kissed her again, then leaned back and stared out the windshield at nothing in particular for a moment.

"Aw, shit," he said. "I'm tired. Let's go."

They drove back to Falmouth in virtual silence except for the music. Mandy's one comment was, "Whatever happens, Dave, I love you." It was weak, she knew, but didn't know what else to say.

David kissed her goodnight at the car, and she went upstairs, brushed her teeth and fell into bed at eleven o'clock, exhausted, but her eyes wouldn't close. Uncertain thoughts flitted through her mind, of past bonfires, of Julie, David, the new job at the club, and college, the great unknown future. Vaguely frightened, she fell into a fitful sleep and dreamed the kind of dreams that insecurity creates. But she wouldn't remember them the next morning.

Chapter Two

The family left Falmouth at six on the morning of September 5th for the University of Maine at Farmington, a single pair of skis and two large cardboard boxes tightly secured to the roof-rack. While they were still driving through town Brad tried to hide his face from early-rising pedestrians. "People are going to think we're crazy, skiing in September," he suggested.

They crossed Cape Cod Canal at Buzzard's Bay before six-thirty and decided to take the longer but quicker Interstate 495 northward to skirt Boston and the rush-hour traffic. The southeastern Massachusetts highway was only lightly traveled in the early morning, and they made good time.

In the back seat of the Pontiac with Brad, Mandy leaned against the door with her left elbow on the armrest and her chin on her hand as she looked out the window, without really seeing the Massachusetts landscape pass before her. Ralph drove without speaking, and Brad contented himself with the latest issue of Popular Mechanics. Conversation seemed forced, awkward. Anne was already talking about Thanksgiving break and wondering whether or not her sister's family in Hartford would be coming over. Some antagonism had resulted from a telephone discussion with Anne over her sister's alcoholic husband and his obnoxious behavior.

"Frankly, my dear, I don't give a damn if they don't come," said Ralph.

Mandy barely noticed their conversation, except for talk of family dissension, which she disliked, or the occasional burst of autumn color that flew by, and wondered why she couldn't say goodbye to David last night. Neither had wanted to hurt the other by saying that dreadful word, and each had pledged to remain faithful to the other, even at long distance. Mandy had felt obligated to go to college, though she really wanted to stay in Falmouth with David. Her dad seemed so proud to have saved enough money to send her. "It's just for your college; don't disappoint us," he'd said. Mandy had heard her father brag to his friends at Rotary that she'd been accepted at three schools. Her parents had such hopes for her, but she hadn't the slightest idea even what to major in. On the applications she wrote in "English" simply because it seemed so easy for her.

David was leaving Falmouth too. As long as Mandy would be going to Farmington, he sent off an application to Thayer Business College in Boston. Only three weeks later he received a letter of acceptance. Mandy had the distinct impression that David was anything but enthusiastic about the prospect, but he'd gone through the motions anyway.

"What the hell," he'd said ruefully. "I can use some economics. Besides, there's an outside chance they know something I don't."

Mandy and David had made a pact. Once a week they would phone, and twice a week—on Tuesdays and Fridays—they would write. They too had already made plans for Thanksgiving break, for as much time together as they could manage in Falmouth. But in her heart Mandy knew Thanksgiving might be the time for her to make a decision whether or not to stay with David. She was vaguely aware that something within her was changing. But it hadn't crossed her mind that David might stray before then as well.

The '62 Grand Prix moved smoothly over the highway, and it seemed to Mandy that a lump of concrete lay in her stomach, and a vague emptiness or ache seemed to spread out from it. Was it because she was already missing David? Or was it the fear of the unknown closing in on her? Or something else? Well, time would tell.

The three weeks with Julie in July had been the ultimate disappointment. Maybe that's what caused the ache. She'd had so much to tell her, had even made a list so she wouldn't forget anything. And more than anything, she wanted to share her secret, that terrible thing that had happened to her in school, with the one person she thought she could talk to. But it wasn't to be.

Mandy couldn't believe the changes in her friend. For as long as she could remember, in Mandy's eyes Julie was much prettier than she, and had the better figure by far. Mandy remembered how all the boys would leer at Julie when they were out shopping or at the movies. With her full bust, narrow waist and lithe hips, not to mention the long blonde hair, she was a stunner. Mandy thought she had to rely on her sense of humor and athletic ability to be attractive; she considered her body barely acceptable, ordinary at best. Though in fact she had a quite beautiful Scandinavian face, with marvelous blue-green eyes, white teeth and a delicate nose offset by a few freckles, she never saw the beauty inherent there. She was anything but satisfied with her looks; nothing was right.

Her mind wandered to the crazy diets and beauty treatments that Julie used to try out on Mandy before using them herself. Mandy loved Julie's worldliness, but after all, she did have two older sisters. Then there was their last sleep-over at Julie's before she'd left for Philadelphia. Mandy's stomach still revolted when she remembered how dizzy and ill the bloody Marys had made her. To this day she was still a bit scared of alcohol after that night....

She had trusted people and things to stay the same, but her first impression of Julie, back in Falmouth, was how much older she looked, how sophisticated and self-confident she appeared. Of course, her big sisters had groomed her from day one, but now she was a real city girl. She was a knockout, with clothes that matched beautifully, perfect make-up and a short Italian hairstyle that enhanced her already remarkable face. She wasn't going to college. She'd landed a job as a model for Crane's Department Store in Philadelphia. She knew what she wanted and where she was going. Mandy felt intimidated, inadequate. She felt as if she were in some sort of competition with Julie and couldn't match up.

Mandy and David had easily persuaded Pete Michaelson, a large, good-looking and likable sort, to ask Julie out. The foursome had gone to a community dance, a beach bonfire party and a drive-in movie together, and Julie had seemed more bored than anything. Her one passion in Falmouth was to lie on the beach at Falmouth Heights, to get a tan that would be the envy of the modeling class at Crane's. Eventually Pete threw in the towel.

One evening after dinner, the sun low in the sky over the water, Mandy sat on the beach with Julie and they tried to talk. Mandy had looked forward to such a time when they could relive their old intimacies and share their heart concerns. There were so many casual, comfortable things they'd done together before— like the time Julie asked Mandy to iron her hair to take the curls out—and still so many things to talk about. In particular, Mandy wanted more than anything to confide in her best friend about the incident that had eaten away at her for some eight months. No one knew about it, even David—no one except Mandy and that man.

But Julie wanted to talk only of two things—her life in Philadelphia, the modeling for Crane's, the wardrobe she had access to, the possibility of being photographed for the cover of Vogue magazine—and of Rob McPherson, who had immediately hit on her the first day she'd visited Mandy at the country club. Julie liked his smile, his tanned and taut body, his talent at tennis, his position at the country club, his potential. And Rob liked her looks and her class. They made quick connection.

Julie's preoccupation with Rob relieved the awkwardness of the changed relationship with Mandy. The new lovers spent a lot of time alone together, at tennis, dinners, movies, and drives along the moonlit beach, which usually ended with passionate love-making and sometimes a late swim. Once Mandy realized that Julie had grown beyond the mundane concerns of life generally and old friends in particular, she appreciated Julie's preoccupations; at least she wouldn't have to entertain an uninterested guest. Even so, Mandy felt a tremendous sense of loss of Julie's friendship and the closeness they shared, and had to resign herself to keeping her secret a private matter. But inside there was a subtle gnawing away at her being. Why? Why couldn't things have stayed the same between them?

Mandy bumped violently against the car door as the Pontiac veered sharply to the right. "Ow! What are you doing, Dad?"

"Sorry, honey," Ralph said.

For the last ten minutes they had been on the New Hampshire Turnpike, and Ralph decided to stop for lunch at Hampton. It was noon and Brad had been complaining for some time that he was starving to death, and it was now grating on Ralph's nerves. He'd tried to make a late exit off the highway and almost missed.

As the car wound eastward toward the center of Hampton,

Mandy remembered driving with David to Hampton Beach two years earlier for the annual Fourth of July celebration among the college crowd. They had narrowly missed being arrested when they'd found themselves next to a raucous and highly intoxicated group of revelers from Portsmouth whose main pleasure seemed to derive from throwing empty beer bottles at couples sitting on the beach. Police had converged as if from nowhere, almost catching the innocent David and Mandy with the drunken troublemakers.

Service was slow at Landers' Tavern, the old landmark restaurant at the center of town. Ralph soon let the waiter know of his impatience, but Anne dismissed his protestations with a curt, "Don't worry about it, Ralph. We're not racing anybody. Consider it a Sunday outing."

"I would, but it's Monday," replied Ralph sullenly. "Besides, I'm starting to get a headache from driving."

"Let me drive, Dad," urged Brad. "This highway's easy."

"Forget it. You've got two more years yet."

On the road back to the highway, Mandy marveled at the plain but stately old houses visible from the car. "They all look like they're three hundred years old. They don't look anything like Falmouth houses."

Anne replied, "Everywhere you go, you'll find that things are different from what we're used to, dear. And it'll be the same in Farmington. But the people are the same everywhere, and that's the important thing."

Mandy suddenly became frightened. She didn't want things to be different. Never mind that she wouldn't know anyone in Maine. Why shouldn't the houses be the same? And now she was learning that even they would be strange and different. She leaned her head back on the seat and closed her eyes. She was troubled, and not just because of unfamiliar houses. Mandy felt an insecurity she hadn't known before.

The Pontiac went up over the Piscataqua River at Portsmouth and down into Maine at Kittery. Ralph complained that there were so many toll booths along the highways, they must have been paid off years ago. But the turnpike was smooth and fast, and traffic moving toward Portland was light. Before long the highway curved slightly, from northeast to due north, bypassing Portland. Some thirty miles farther, they made the exit to Lewiston, where a two-lane road carried them another fifty miles finally to Farmington. They turned right at the town's main intersection and continued for several blocks. Huge shade trees, bright with autumn color, lined the street. The short line of stores ended and small, old houses, set back from the street, took their place for a short distance. Suddenly large white houses, with thick Grecian columns supporting overhanging roofs, appeared on both sides of the road. Greek letters over the doorways indicated these were fraternity or sorority houses. Four or five shirtless young men tossed a football on the expansive lawn of one of the houses.

They passed a large sign at roadside that read, "University of Maine, established 1864." Massive brick buildings, named either for academic disciplines or people, loomed next to the roads. Tall pine trees, located in well-designed disarray, stood in groves and as single specimens on the sparse lawns, allowing only a patchwork of sunlight to reach the ground in places. The campus appeared somewhat dark even with the sun bright in the clear, afternoon sky. They came to a low, brick building with a U-shaped driveway and a correspondingly low sign in front that read "Administration." Mandy was a bit relieved to see other young people among the cars and on the sidewalk, some with their parents. Well, at least I'm not the only new one here, Mandy thought. The family accompanied her to the Information counter, where she picked up a college catalogue and a packet of brochures and papers dealing mostly with orientation to the campus. Walking back to the car, she peered closely at a small map, then pointed to a little rectangle. "Here's Craig Hall."

Dad maneuvered the car out of the parking lot, onto the street and drove slowly toward Craig Hall, Mandy's dormitory. Their heads craned this way and that, trying to take in everything. They made two lefts and found themselves at the dorm, a three-story brick building with a massive double-door entrance and columns on either side. It was only three blocks or so from the edge of downtown Farmington.

"Walking distance," noted Ralph.

"Good thing," Brad offered. "Any more than two blocks and she'd have to call a cab."

"Stop it, Bratley," pleaded Mandy. "Can't you ever be nice?"

Mandy and her mother went in to the reception area to check in while Ralph and Brad struggled with what seemed to them extraordinarily excessive luggage. Besides the suitcases and two large boxes were the skis and boots, a lamp, a pillow with ruffles, a large blue teddy bear, two tennis rackets, two framed pictures of family members, a tube of rolled wall posters and a small floor rug, most of it crammed into the car's trunk. They were grateful at least that Mandy's room, 252 East Wing, was only on the second floor. Still, the men required three trips to move all of her paraphernalia inside.

Mandy would be sharing the room with three other girls, also new freshmen. Only one had arrived, Joanne Gilman, from West Lebanon in southern Maine, near the New Hampshire border. She was a big girl, "from the farm—hay and tads," she said. Joanne had dark hair and a pretty face. She was slow to smile, but when she did, it was striking, the picture of farm-fresh health. Mandy felt certain they'd hit it off.

The dorm room looked nothing like a hospital ward, as Mandy had expected. Her image of a college dorm consisted of a dozen or more beds lined side by side against each wall, with nothing separating them but two feet of space, a picture she'd seen in the movies. Here, however, a free-standing wall partition split the room into two smaller sections, each an almost private room for two. When someone entered through the door, she could go left or right into either of the sections. In each, one bed sat against the far wall and another against the inside partition; neither the beds nor the two work desks, crammed into the corners against the outside wall, afforded a direct view out of—or in through—the window in the center. And each section had two dressers with mirrors on top and a large walk-in closet, which had to be shared with a roommate, against the corridor wall. A good-sized bathroom, also against the corridor wall, completed the apartment. The spotless walls, carpets, curtains and bathroom were finished in a tasteful, relaxing peach and off-white color combination. This is nice and cozy, thought Mandy, amazed and pleased at how comfortable her new surroundings appeared.

Joanne had taken a bed against the far wall and away from the bathroom. She explained to Mandy that after years of early mornings on the farm, she wanted to get some real sleep here, without the distraction of a continually flushing toilet. Mandy appreciated her wisdom and decided to join her in the left section. Ralph and Brad deposited Mandy's things on her bed and on the floor while she and Anne found places to put them. After the last load, the two men watched the women for a moment, then Ralph said, "Time's getting on, Anne. What do you say we find a nice place for dinner? Maybe we should let her finish this later."

"Okay," Mandy said in approval. "It'll take me a while to figure out where everything goes anyway. Dad, would it be all right if Joanne could come with us?"

Joanne declined, suggesting the family should be together for Mandy's last evening with them; besides, there would be plenty of time together for the two girls. So the four went down and out to the car, where several other families were going through the same process of unloading equally astonishing quantities of personal belongings. Ralph just shook his head as he drove off.

It was eight-thirty when they pulled up to Craig Hall after dinner. There was no need to say goodbye quite yet, as the family would stay in a motel at the edge of town—except Mandy, who wanted to get situated in the dorm. They would have an early breakfast together before the others started back to Cape Cod. As the car drove off to the motel, Mandy stood in the darkening evening and waved. Then she went in to get to know her new roommate and put her things away. She felt an uncontrollable urge to arrange things, to feel right about her new surroundings. Somehow, it seemed to be very important to her to do that, to make her surroundings her own. At eleven-thirty she set the music alarm and climbed into bed. It took her a long time to fall asleep.

Saying goodbye after breakfast the next morning was awkward for everyone. Outside the car back at Craig Hall, Ralph kissed Mandy on the cheek as he pushed a couple of folded bills into her hand. "For an emergency," he said. Only Anne hugged Mandy, and only after a stern "Do you want to walk back to Falmouth?" did Brad give his sister a peck on the cheek. Nobody really knew what to say.

"You call me collect any time, dear," Mom said.

"But not too often," rejoined Ralph.

"We better get going," Brad said, leaning on the door handle.

Mandy tried to smile and said, "Thanks for everything. Have a safe drive back. And if you see David, if he hasn't left yet, ask him to write right away."

Anne smiled and gave Mandy another hug. "We will, dear. Here's a little bag of goodies in case you get hungry."

"Thanks, Mom. Gee, you think of everything," Mandy replied, on the verge of tears.

"Well, we'd better get going," Ralph repeated.

Again they got into the car. Each one rolled down a window as Ralph started the motor. There was a chorus of 'Bye's and waves as the Pontiac again moved out of the driveway and onto the street. Mandy stood on the pavement and waved until the car turned a corner and went out of view. She brushed away tears and stood there a moment, still looking at the empty corner where the car had disappeared. She glanced up at the brown, falling leaves, then turned and went inside.

The two other girls arrived at the dorm the following day, Tuesday. Barbara Connors, a dark-haired girl from Presque Isle, was quiet and serious and also quite pretty, in a plain sort of way. Her father owned a hardware store, and her mother, who did the bookkeeping for the family business, had trained her as much as she could in financial matters. Barbara would major in business administration.

The last addition to the dorm room was Linda Harney, a short, pert, lively girl and a Christian, who had spent two years in Minnesota in a Bible college just after graduation from high school. Her home was in Portland. Mandy asked her why she'd enrolled at the Farmington campus and not at Portland-Gorham, which was just a short distance from where she lived.

"That's too close to home," she said, smiling. "This is far enough away, but not too far."

Mandy wondered why Minnesota wasn't too far away, but didn't ask.

Registration, the feared process of obtaining the semester's courses, began Wednesday morning. Seniors had to worry that courses they needed for graduation would still be open by the time their names were scheduled in line. Freshmen, who registered last, were afraid that their introductory courses would be closed. Freshmen and sophomores, of course, couldn't normally enroll in advanced courses, as these often required certain introductory prerequisite courses. The greatest fear among the lower classmen was that not enough courses would be available for them to carry a full load of five classes. A typical comment was, "My folks will kill me if they find out I've only got three classes."

To give everyone a fair chance, the registrar picked letters of the alphabet at random; students were to register according to their class level and in the order that the letters appeared on the boards, which were placed at strategic places so that every student would know what was happening. As it happened, all the girls in Mandy's dorm room could start registering on Thursday afternoon.

Both in the middle of the freshman list, Barbara and Mandy, whose last names began with C, decided to go through registration together. First, they went to the Ad Building for their registration packets, which held the necessary materials—IBM cards, course schedule, notes about course changes and the like. Then they went over to the men's gym.

Mandy and Barbara found themselves standing in line for forty-five minutes before they were allowed to enter the gym. Inside was a madhouse. Tables and classroom desks seemed to be everywhere, arranged in some kind of insane order. Signs with names, letters and instructions hung from the walls, and a thousand students milled around and wandered, as if in shock, from place to place to stand in line. Lines were everywhere. This was all very confusing. Mandy hated crowds and wondered how anyone could decide the future in one hectic afternoon. Everyone seemed so frantic, so urgent in their scramble to pick up what was left of the courses. The girls managed to find two empty desks and sat down together to hastily look over the course schedule and compare the offerings to the ever-growing list of closed courses that appeared on the huge board above them.

Mandy found an open biology course, which required a lab. Quickly she scoured the lab listings, and, after checking the overhead board, gave grateful thanks to the Almighty, having located one in a vacant time slot. She then flipped through the pages to the history section. Again she was in luck; and this one was even held at a civilized hour. Time was critical here; each minute spent in the catalogue meant that another course could close at any second. Almost in a panic she flipped the pages, trying to find English. She glanced at the times English 101, the first course, was offered. Her finger ran down the list as she checked the section options, their days and times, and finally the professor's name. Then, in horror, she saw the name "Farquhar."

Lightning seemed to stab through her body. She shot straight back against the chair.

"No!" she blurted involuntarily. "It couldn't be."

Barbara turned and saw her staring in shock at the course schedule.

"What's the matter?" she asked. "Are you okay?"

Her eyes riveted on the booklet, Mandy suddenly realized Barbara's concern and groped for words. After a short pause she said, "No, it's okay. I just, uh..., it's okay. I'm all right."

"Are you sure?"

"Sure. I, uh, just thought I saw something. But it's okay. I guess I was wrong... How are you coming with your list?"

Barbara looked at her for a moment, wondering. "I'm about finished. Are you sure you're okay?"

"Oh, I'm fine. I've just got to put in this English course, then I'm done."

"Well," Barbara said, still a bit worried, "let's finish up. Do you want to try the lines now?"

"Sure. Let's go. I can finish this in line."

This was really stupid, she thought. There's no way in the world this could be the same man. She tried to put it out of her mind as she stood at the back of the line for biology.

Chapter Three

The first two weeks at Farmington were so full of new experiences for Mandy that she didn't have time to be homesick. Classes, as usual, had started off rather slowly and so there was no academic pressure yet. There was a boisterous, exuberant feeling on campus, of being released from parental bondage and the drudgery of meaningless, demeaning summer jobs. The students, especially the freshmen, had entered a whole new world seemingly free of any constraints but their own. None of the instructors even took attendance. For many of them, for the first time in their lives they were their own people. And they lived it up.

Dorm life in particular had its restrictions (there were sign-out and sign-in sheets, and the outside door was bolted at eleven o'clock on week nights), but there were compensations as well. Once the girls got to know each other a little, they found a lot in common to talk about, to laugh about. Generally, doors to the rooms remained open far into the night as groups of two and three moved from one room to another with cookies and other treats left by parents. There were new friends to make, wardrobes and room decors to envy, music to hear, and above all, things to talk about, even to scream about. Sleep was impossible. Life in the dorm seemed like an endless pajama party.

Mandy had problems adjusting to this new freedom. Her world in Falmouth had been so sheltered and predictable. She was used to the privacy of her own room without the constant distractions of dorm life. But she found it terribly exciting, and she didn't want to miss out on any of it.

The boys, of course, carried on much as the girls did. Typically, it was they—especially the frats—who organized "keggers" on the front lawns of their houses. Keggers were great ice-breakers, and they took hardly no effort to organize. One had simply to pick up three or four kegs of beer at a tavern, arrange them on the tailgate of a pickup truck in the driveway, install a pump and tap, place the largest stereo speakers in the house on the front porch, turn on the rock and roll, and it was a party. Keggers commonly didn't require invitations. A fraternity would make a point to invite a certain sorority or girls' dorm, but usually everyone with half a notion would stop by for free beer and the remote possibility of scoring.

Word of a kegger would spread like wildfire. By nine o'clock, with the Beach Boys or the recently arrived Beatles entertaining the whole neighborhood, perhaps two hundred people would be trampling the lawns of several adjacent houses and crowding the street, preventing any movement of traffic at all. Surprisingly there were few complaints, but if there were, the police would simply drive by, look stern and ask that the music and the ruckus be kept down. Life was good in this little college town.

Around 10:30 at the dorm one night in late September, Mandy heard screams in the hall. Terrified, she stopped ironing her blouse and yanked the cord from the wall. She pulled her bathrobe close about her and went to the door, where she heard heavy footsteps pounding past. Someone screamed, "Man on the floor! Panty raid!"

She opened the door, and a young man wearing a trench coat and a Robin Hood hat pushed roughly past her and raced to Joanne's dresser, where he threw open the drawers, reached in and grabbed a handful of underwear, a bra and several pairs of panties. Stunned, Joanne watched in disbelief for a brief moment and then yelled, "Hey, you son of a bitch, get the fuck out of my drawers! Give me back my undies, Godammit!"

She jumped up to hit him, but he ducked his head and raced out the door with a loud "Whoop!" waving his prizes. Shocked, wide-eyed, and briefly wondering in her mind if she could ever swear like that, Mandy followed Joanne out into the hall and the midst of pandemonium. Girls in their nighties and bathrobes were running to their rooms; boys, dressed in everything from cut-off jeans and hockey helmets to long underwear and raincoats, were running in and out of rooms and down the hallway, hollering and laughing. Joanne, with Mandy trailing, ran to the stairway and down to the first floor where girls, some half dressed, were running with buckets of water, screaming and swearing.

A young man wearing a ski mask pulled over his face ran past them, clutching a radio. Another boy squirted a tube of toothpaste along the wall as he ran down the hallway. Underwear and other pieces of clothing lay scattered on the floor where they'd been dropped. The house mother, a fragile, grey-haired woman in her mid-60s, appeared from her apartment overlooking the stairwell. She was apparently the last one to know what was happening.

"Lock all the doors, ladies! Lock the windows!" she screamed, waving her arms.

As the last of the boys ran from the dorm, streaming underwear behind them, many of the girls on the first floor still carried buckets of water to their rooms to throw at any feckless male head that appeared at their windows.

By 10:35 the panty raid was over. Mandy was grateful that hers was a second-story room. She hadn't lost anything in the fracas. Joanne was the room's only victim, and Mandy had only the greatest sympathy for her plight, for having lost her favorite bra and a very expensive and sexy pair of panties. Somehow, the whole matter was too funny to be serious, though Joanne disagreed vociferously, and the other girls had a good laugh. Before going to bed, however, the girls decided how they would defend themselves against the next raid, promising among themselves to defend their door with every means at hand, even to using their ski-poles.

Late that evening, Mandy wrote a short letter to David, but didn't mention the evening's panty raid, the parties or keggers she'd attended with her dorm friends. No need to upset him.

By the end of September, most students had settled into the routine of classes and studies. Weekends, of course, were considered well-deserved breaks, a time for letting the hair down on and off campus. But one often learned the hard way to be moderate with partying. Mandy, caught up in the boisterous activities of her friends in the dorm, had to learn the hard way. She tried to participate fully in the enormously attractive social activities that went on around her, while at the same time having a full load of courses—biology, philosophy, English, French, history, and gymnastics—with the attendant homework they required. She had done quite well in high school, with A's and B's in most subjects, but that had taken hard work and the persistent supervision of her parents. As the weeks progressed, with only her inexperienced conscience as a guide, she found herself far behind in her studies. When test time came in history and biology, she discovered that college was much tougher than high school. She flunked both mid-term exams.

Mandy also allowed herself to be talked into a foolish Thursday trip down to Freeport with Joanne and another girl to shop for hiking boots—standard equipment for student "Manlacs"— at the famous L.L. Bean's store. In doing so, she missed a surprise English test that Dr. Downey sprang on the class. Thus, when she returned that evening and discovered she'd missed her test, she became frightened. Early Friday morning she rushed over to the English building to see Dr. Downey about taking a make-up test. The building was actually called Henry Wadsworth Longfellow Hall, in honor of the poet who'd lived and written some of his famous works in Maine. The girls in the dorm called it Hard-on Hall, as a play on Longfellow. They joked about the English professors, most of whom were quite meek, but the girls made the most of their pun. "Don't bend over in Hard-on Hall, girls," was the common warning. But Mandy saw no humor in it today.

Formulating the details of a lie about having stomach flu and therefore having to miss class, Mandy approached Longfellow Hall scared half to death. She entered the nearest door and hurried up the stairs to Dr. Downey's office on the third floor. Classes were on, but she knew Dr. Downey had office hours at this time. Please, God, let no one else be in his office, she pleaded. She reached the third floor quite out of breath and walked toward his office. Ten steps into the corridor, she stopped short and froze. Coming toward her, but not yet seeing her, was Gordon Farquhar, professor of English. With folders in one hand, he reached out with the other to open his office door. Then, for some reason, he looked up and saw Mandy, standing stock still, only twenty feet away. Surprised himself, after a moment his stone face took on a wry smile, and he turned fully to face her, saying nothing. Mandy stood there, dumbfounded, her mouth stupidly open, unable to move. "Oh God, no," she said involuntarily. Then she turned and ran back to the stairway and down. "No, no, no," she kept repeating as she ran out of the building and onto the sidewalk, tears of anger and confusion streaming down her cheeks.

Mandy walked aimlessly, wherever the sidewalk led. Hands shoved deep in her coat pockets, she looked up through the tree branches and the few remaining leaves and was blinded by the sun and her tears. "Why, God? How could he be here?" It was so unfair. The thing she'd tried most to put out of her life now sprang to life before her. She shook her head violently, gritting her teeth, feeling anger and fear. Discouraged and cold, she decided just to go back to her room. Escape was all she could think of, but the memory engulfed her. Her secret had followed her to Farmington.

Chapter Four

Dr. Gordon Farquhar was Mandy's English teacher in her senior year at Falmouth High. He was thirty, tall and very good-looking, with dark hair, chiseled features and sensitive brown eyes, and he had a ready, winning smile. He was married and the father of two boys seven and nine years old. His wife Beverly was a stunning blonde, also about thirty, who frequented Tecumseh Country Club at Falmouth Heights for both golf and tennis, but rarely in the company of her husband. Quiet rumors had it that Rob McPherson and Beverly Farquhar had more in common than an affinity for tennis.

Mandy's solid achievements in biology at Falmouth prompted Mr. Walters, her lab teacher, to ask if she'd like to be student lab assistant for the fall term. Delighted, she had accepted. Her main job was to make sure the mouse and rabbit cages were clean, that pellets were placed in the little feed containers, and there was fresh water. Mandy loved the little white mice more than the rabbits—they were small, soft and cuddly, and they responded to her care. The rabbits were lovable, but they were fat and never moved except, when they felt like it, to sidle half a step and rearrange their hind feet under themselves.

The mice, however, seemed to have personality. Almost as if they were tiny pets, like small puppies, they would move to whichever side of the cage Mandy was on and stand up with their miniature, exquisitely formed forefeet against the wire mesh of the cage, curious and straining to get close to her.

A short time after classes ended one day and when almost everyone had gone, Mandy happened to be walking to the Bio Lab when Dr. Farquhar passed her in the hall on the way to his office. He nodded and smiled as they passed each other. Out of courtesy Mandy returned the smile. She stopped at the door of the lab, took out her key and entered the room to clean the cages, leaving the door ajar. After a few moments, without her noticing, Farquhar walked quietly into the lab and carefully closed the door. She turned to see him walking around the end of the long table, piled with cages and containers. He smiled and said "hello," and she returned the greeting. Without thinking, she went back to adding pellets to the rabbit feeder, her back toward him.

Then Mandy felt something brush her back. Before she could move, his strong hands gripped her waist firmly, and she felt his warm breath on her skin. She stiffened as his lips pressed against her neck. Holding her tightly so she couldn't move, he shoved his body hard against her from behind. She felt him thrust his hips rudely against her buttocks, moving from side to side, up and down, pushing into her. She was against the cages and couldn't turn, couldn't move. Too stunned to fight, she stiffened as his hands moved up to grasp her breasts, his lips still on her neck, as he tried to read her body for any response. Terrified, she wanted to turn, to try to run, to resist the rush of sensations within her. Suddenly, frantically, she twisted, wrenched out of his grasp. She dropped the rabbit pellets, uttering a feeble "Excuse me," and bolted around the lab table and out the door without looking back. Shaken with fear, she half walked, half ran home, curiously concerned about the rabbits and mice. She told no one.

In bed that evening Mandy battled confusion, mixed messages. This man was a teacher, an adult, someone she'd looked up to, so knowledgeable, so worldly. She'd liked his classes, even though he was demanding. He would have all the girls on the edge of their seats when he read aloud. His voice was so rich and sonorous, and he knew it. And the comments he'd written on her creative writing essay back in September made her feel so mature, and he'd praised her for her sensitivity and imaginative style. But had he been wanting her all that time? How could she have missed the signs? Were there any signs? Had she done or said anything to make him approach her this way? He knew about David. He'd seen them together on several occasions. But he's married!

"Oh God, please help me," she pleaded. She felt unclean, wicked, without knowing why.

The next day in English class Mandy kept her eyes on her desk, out the window, anywhere but on Gordon Farquhar. She couldn't look at him but somehow knew his eyes swept over her at regular intervals. She sat nervously, weakly, fingers entwining endlessly, fiddling with a ball-point pen, unable to concentrate. Dr. Farquhar rose from his desk to pass back the poetry notebooks amid moans and groans from the students. She watched him walk to the first desk; he was saying, "These weren't as bad as I'd originally expected, but some of you had better take a close look at my marginal notes. And if you think you'd like to come see me, by all means, do. We'll talk about it." As he moved from desk to desk, she knew he was watching her surreptitiously. He placed her notebook on her desk and moved to another student. Then the bell rang. Dr. Farquhar passed out the two remaining notebooks, and everyone got up to leave. Mandy tried to hide in the crowd as they moved to the door. He said nothing as she left.

Mandy went into the girls' bathroom, found an empty booth, went in and locked the door. She sat down and opened the notebook. Opening the cover she saw, beneath the title on the first page, the scrawled comment, "Excellent work— A+ Keep it up." Quickly she leafed through the pages in search of writing in the margins. There was nothing. Then she noticed something inserted between two pages. She pulled out a small piece of paper with only a poem on it. With shaking hands she looked at it without really reading—words about spring, and love, gentleness, beauty, softness, pleasure. How did he know that these things meant so much to her? There was no name, no signature. Quickly she pushed it back into the notebook, threw open the door and went out of the bathroom. Mandy felt terrible confusion, fear mixed with emotions she couldn't identify. What am I supposed to do? she wondered.

In the days that followed, Farquhar worked subtly on Mandy, trying to draw her to himself. Beginning with his passing out the poetry notebooks, his lectures would be full of double entendres, apparently simple, straightforward statements, but Mandy clearly heard the messages in them addressed to her. Still in the poetry section of the course, Farquhar quoted from the Song of Solomon, as an example of poetry from the Bible. He leaned back on the front of his desk, directly in front of Mandy who was three seats back, and read:

"Behold, thou art fair, my love; behold thou art fair. Thou

hast doves' eyes within thy locks; thy hair is as a flock of goats that appear from Mount Gilead. Thy teeth are like a flock of sheep that are even shorn, which came up from the washing, of which every one beareth twins, and none is barren among them.

"Thy lips are like a thread of scarlet, and thy speech is comely; thy temples are like a piece of pomegranate within thy locks. Thy neck is like the tower of David builded for an armory, on which there hang a thousand bucklers, all shields of mighty men.

"Thy two breasts are like two young roes that are twins, which feed among the lilies. Until the day break, and the shadows flee away, I will go up to the mountain of myrrh, and to the hill of frankincense.

"Thou art all fair, my love; there is no spot in thee."

When Farquhar finished he looked up briefly at Mandy, then glanced around at other class members and asked what it meant. She knew what this poem meant and to whom it was directed. Hah, she thought. He just doesn't know about the scar on my head. She fought a rising blush and hoped with all her heart that no one would notice her discomfort.

Mandy would try to concentrate on her work in class, but somehow she knew it didn't matter; whatever she produced, she would get an A. Farquhar would tell Mandy and at least one other person to stay after class. He would have something to say to the other student, then dismiss him or her. Then in private together, he would turn to Mandy and bend to kiss her and tell her he loved her. She felt that his eyes penetrated her soul as he looked at her.

Somehow she had to do what he told her. He was a teacher, her teacher, and therefore was in a position of power over her. At his command she stayed after school. In his office he would force her, somehow willingly, but also against her will, to submit to his advances. He would touch her intimately, both exciting her physically and deeply offending her as he moved his hands over her body. She hated it, and somehow, perversely, she almost loved it. He kept pressing, pressing. Once, when he drove five students to a community play, she sat behind him in the far left of the rear passenger seat, where he'd told her to sit. Later, riding in the darkness she felt his left hand reach behind the seat and move up her leg under her dress. He aroused and excited her, but at the same time she felt victimized, molested. She was disgusted at the way her own body betrayed her, at the pleasure she felt in each caress. She felt trapped, and she began to hate herself.

As the days went on she became more frightened, more confused. She knew it was only a matter of time before he tried something worse. There was no one she could turn to; how could she ever tell this to anyone?

After several weeks of clandestine meetings, Mandy started to become withdrawn into herself. She tried to pretend that nothing was wrong, and she succeeded in deceiving everyone but herself. Then on a Tuesday, two weeks before semester's end, a substitute teacher showed up in English. He announced that he would be with the students until the holidays; Dr. Farquhar was ill and would be out for the rest of the term. Mandy felt great relief until she heard the kids talking after class. Ellen's mother, also a teacher at Falmouth High, had heard that Farquhar had contracted infectious hepatitis. Ellen confirmed that he would be out for at least a month.

More frightened than ever, Mandy went home that night and tried nonchalantly to approach the subject with her own mother, a registered nurse, as they did the dishes.

"Mom, is infectious hepatitis contagious?"

"Why would you ask me that?" she asked with a little laugh.

"Oh, we just heard that one of the teachers has it," Mandy said, "and we were just curious, that's all."

"Well, you can tell everyone to relax. You won't get it from a teacher."

With that reassurance Mandy was able to make it through Christmas break, though she couldn't bring herself to tell Julie about Farquhar's attentions during her short visit. And of course, she could never tell David or her parents. Before the next term began she changed English classes and by some miracle somehow evaded Gordon Farquhar for the rest of the year. But the issue was never quite resolved as time went on, and she'd told no one. She bore the shame, the guilt, the confusion, all the terrible feelings by herself. It continued to slowly eat away at her.

Mandy walked slowly back to Craig Hall, painful memories of Gordon Farquhar fresh in her mind. And now he was here, at Farmington! My God, why? How did he get here? Of all the colleges in the country, why did I pick Farmington? This was the ultimate bad dream. Where are you, God? Where are you when I need you? She looked up and saw the bare branches of the trees as a chilly breeze from the northwest stung her tear-stained cheeks. She pulled up the collar on her coat and walked on, only vaguely aware of her direction.

Linda Harney was making her way across the lawn in front of Craig Hall when she spotted Mandy cross the road to the dorm. She could tell something was wrong when Mandy blindly stepped off the curb without looking up for traffic. Linda changed direction and met her at the curb, her eyes red from crying.

"Hey, what's wrong? Can I help?" Linda offered.

Mandy mumbled something inaudibly, then looked up and realized it was Linda. Of her three roommates she knew the least about Linda, but something about her led Mandy to accompany her up the stairs and into their room. The other roommates were away, and they went into the section Linda shared with Barbara. Linda dropped her books on her desk, kicked off her shoes and sat on the edge of the bed. Mandy watched in silence. She didn't know what to say, yet she didn't want to go.

"I don't know if I can help, but I'm a pretty good listener," Linda smiled warmly.

Mandy's chin quivered as tears welled up inside. All that came out was, "I'm so miserable. I just want to die."

Linda responded immediately. She jumped up from the bed and wrapped her arms around Mandy as more tears came. "Come on and sit down," she said, gently guiding Mandy to sit on the edge of the bed. She handed Mandy a tissue.

Mandy sniffled and wiped her nose and her eyes. "I can't believe I'm such a jerk. I don't deserve to be here," she stammered.

Linda said, "Just tell me to shut up if you don't want to hear. I'm used to people shutting me off. But I know you're supposed to be here. We've all got a place here. We've all got a really important job to do. I know God wants nothing but the best for you. He loves you. He promised in the Bible that if anyone believes in Jesus and trusts in him to take care of any problem, he would never leave that person. He would always be there to love you and listen to you, to handle just anything that troubles you. All you have to do is ask him into your heart and trust that Jesus will give you whatever you need to overcome it."

When Mandy heard that, she really didn't want to hear any more, but she wasn't brave enough to say so. Mandy's family had never been very religious. Both she and Brad had gone to Sunday school as kids, but no one had ever forced church attendance on them. Mandy believed in God; she often prayed at night for mankind to stop the fighting, for world peace. But she never felt right about asking for too much. She never once thought she could have a personal relationship with God. But as Linda talked, Mandy found herself calmer and more relaxed.

Linda suddenly felt that Mandy had drifted off, that she might have offended her.

"I'm sorry if I come across strong in my faith. I don't mean to preach. You see, a classmate of mine actually did kill herself. Almost three years ago now. That's one reason I went to Bible college in Minnesota. I had a very hard time accepting that, but believing and trusting in God has really made a difference in my life. And I know now that to take your own life is really a sin. And God loves you so much. Please believe me when I say that God wants you to live. He wants to help you be happy. He sent his son Jesus to die for you, to make you whole."

Mandy reached over and gave her a hug this time. "I'm sorry, Linda. Please forgive me for frightening you. I do feel better now. I guess I was feeling pretty desperate. I really don't want to kill myself." She tried to smile. "Thanks for your help. I guess I'll work things out somehow."

Chapter Five

Despite Mandy's initial reluctance to move away to college—away from the comfortable security of home, family and David—and the perpetual fear of Gordon Farquhar's turning up at any moment, she really enjoyed college. She simply decided to change her major and stay as far away as possible from the English building.

She was almost overwhelmed with her new freedom, the excitement and adventure that seemed to grow with every week of this new life. The girls of Craig Hall seemed devoted to getting the most out of college life. There were football games and parties outside town on the bank of the river, intramural sports and fraternity parties, bike rides and private parties, weekend dances and parties afterwards, canoe outings and more parties. There were street dances, spaghetti suppers, movies, costume parades—an endless round of diversions from studying.

It was a simple matter for Mandy, as one of the several hundred Craig girls, to become caught up in the whirl of life at UMF, to go with the flow. She loved the camaraderie. Being one of the girls, really belonging, helped to overcome some of her underlying insecurities. But now they didn't matter so much; she was really having a good time. The weeks flew by in rounds of classes and partying and generally having fun. Aside from the gnawing prospect of Gordon Farquhar's showing up at any time and the occasional twinge of guilt about letting her parents down by slacking off on her studies, the only problem was her grades; she was flunking three courses.

Late one afternoon in the middle of October Mandy returned from class to the dorm. Her roommates greeted her with broad grins and strange comments. "Is there someone we ought to know about?" asked Barbara.

"Well, Mandy, come on. Who is it?" Joanne wanted to know.

Linda said nothing. From the moment it arrived she had

assumed that the box on Mandy's bed was somehow connected with her "problem."

Mandy was simply confused. "What's going on here, you guys?" She looked at them strangely, then went to her bed and tossed her books down. It was then that she noticed a long rectangular box on the bed. "Delivery said it was for you. Open it, Mandy," urged Joanne.

With the girls crowded excitedly around the bed, Mandy bent down and slipped off the thin plastic tie, lifted off the cover and unfolded the waxy tissue that covered the contents. There, carefully arranged, lay a dozen beautiful long-stemmed yellow roses.

"Oh, how neat," Joanne said, her hands clapped on her cheeks.

"They're beautiful!" said Barbara. "Who sent them? Where's the card?"

Mandy couldn't believe her eyes. Astonished, she found the little white envelope tucked into the stems and opened it. The words said simply, "Thou art fair, my love."

"Well, who are they from?" pressed Joanne.

"Uh, I don't know," Mandy blurted. "There's no signature." Linda took the card from her hand and read it. Mandy turned away and stared out the window, seeing nothing. She felt trapped, scared. He's after me again, and he knows where I live, she thought angrily.

"I don't want these things." She waved her hand upward toward the box, as if to sweep them away.

"Someone please take them out of here, will you please?" she begged.

"Why? They're beautiful, Mandy." Joanne responded, perplexed.

"Well, they're from someone I don't want anything to do with," Mandy said. "Please take them out of here."

She started to cry. Curiously, her mind shot back to a time when she was ill as a little girl. In a high fever and almost delirious, she had lain in bed convinced she was hearing loud, booming voices threaten her: "Coming to get you! Coming to get you!" they repeated over and over.

Mandy tried to stifle the tears.

Linda picked up the box and took it down to the lobby, where a number of girls were hanging around just before the dinner bell. She held up the box and announced in a loud voice, "Whoever lives in West Wing and wants some roses, here they are. Somebody take them."

She didn't have to ask twice. In a flash they were gone with two girls who skipped back into West Wing with their treasure, delighted with their good fortune.

Confused, the girls in room 252 went down to dinner together with Mandy. They said nothing more about the roses or their thoughtful sender, though they were curious about whom this "someone" could be. Mandy offered no explanation; she kept her secret to herself.

In the days that followed, Farquhar made no other advances.

Tremendously relieved, Mandy resigned again to change her major but couldn't decide what else to concentrate in. Well, she mused, there's plenty of time to decide. She succeeded in evading Gordon Farquhar on campus; she'd simply looked into the course schedule for his weekly class assignments and avoided the buildings he was in during those times, or the walkways he might be using. She was pleased with her success, and also that Farquhar apparently hadn't tried to contact her since sending the flowers. If he thought for one second that she would deliberately go over to see him just because he sent her some flowers, he was absolutely crazy. Cynically, Mandy decided he must have some other victim on his hook. Well, if so, at least it's someone else this time—so far, anyway.

The weeks went by, and one November day the entire campus went into shock and mourning as everyone learned that President Kennedy had been assassinated in Dallas. But the next day everything seemed to be normal again, except for the flag outside the Ad Building; it was at half mast and remained so for a week.

On the whole, classes continued as usual, and Thanksgiving break snuck up on Mandy almost before she realized it. She wanted desperately to pull up her grades before having to face her parents. She felt quite good about her performance on the exams of the past few days; at least B's, she thought. Those will help. But thoughts of going home to David and the family outweighed her apprehensions about academic things. And she didn't want to upset her family's plans for a Thursday afternoon Thanksgiving dinner. A day early, therefore, on Wednesday she left the Farmington Trailways depot, already crowded with a growing student exodus, to arrive in Boston before noon. Tired from late-night studies and pre-holiday exams, Mandy easily fell asleep on the bus, its gentle rocking motion and the hum of wheels on the highway making her relaxed and drowsy. During the rest stop at Portland she stayed in her seat and dozed, waking only briefly when the bus pulled out of the depot.

Mandy awoke some time later and thought of David. She must apologize for not writing him within the last week or more, but then, she could tell him everything in person. Besides, she wanted to tease him because his last two letters had been so brief. They had changed some since he first began writing, but she couldn't put her finger on the difference. They'd also arrived further apart over the last few weeks. Well, hers were becoming less frequent as well; college was just busy for both of them, she rationalized.

At just 11:45 the bus rolled into the depot at Boston.

Cramped after sleeping in an uncomfortable position, Mandy walked stiffly off the last step into the crowd and spied her father and Brad making their way toward her. The men gave her a quick hug and off they went for a quick lunch. Mandy was ravished.

"Where's Mom?" she asked as they walked toward the car.

"She's still baking, couldn't leave," Ralph explained. "She wanted everything to be ready for your homecoming, and her sister's bunch. She's been working on it for days."

"You'd think the president was coming instead of you," Brad said, not unkindly. "But you ought to smell that place. I can't wait. Come on, let's get some food."

By the way, how are you, Brad?" Mandy asked.

"Okay, I guess. But hungry. We've been waiting forty-five minutes."

"Sorry," Mandy said out of habit more than anything.

The ride to the Cape took a bit longer than planned, with traffic unusually heavy before the long weekend. Time passed quickly, however, as Mandy filled the men in on her censored version of college life. The sights and smells became more familiar as they reached the bridge at Buzzard's Bay, and Mandy rolled down her window to see if she could smell the ocean. Half an hour later they pulled up to the house and Ralph tooted the horn. Anne appeared at the door wiping her hands and with a cheery "Welcome home!" waving her dish towel. She and Mandy embraced, the men grabbed her tote bag and suitcase and they went inside to the delicious aroma of Thanksgiving preparations. Here and there Mandy saw the little touches of love her mother had prepared for her—family photos set out, little gifts brought out from past birthdays, dishes of homemade Thanksgiving treats. It's great to be home, she thought.

Mandy went upstairs to call David, but the line was busy. She would try a few minutes later but felt an immediate need for a shower. Excited to see him, she quickly doffed her clothes and stepped under the steaming jets of water. Afterward, she called his house and learned he was still in Boston and would be arriving that evening. He'd call when he got home.

Later that afternoon Mandy drove to the beach at the Heights and walked along the hard sand of low tide. With a slight chill in the air she didn't stay for long, but she enjoyed the comforting sound of the waves, as she had for so many years. Her thoughts ran to the many times she and David had walked along these same sands. She couldn't wait to see him.

After dinner Mandy received a call from the Slone household—David had had some sort of trouble leaving Boston and would get home at noon tomorrow. He'd call as soon as he arrived. With Ralph and Brad engrossed in the football game, Mandy and Anne talked long into the night. Mandy shared only the socially acceptable parts of life at Farmington. Afterward, in her own bed once again, she had difficulty falling asleep.

David finally called Mandy at 1:30 the following day. His family was about to have Thanksgiving dinner, but he'd pick her up at seven o'clock for a drive. That was fine, Mandy lied. She was vaguely annoyed at him for keeping her waiting, though no doubt it wasn't really his fault.

That morning the relatives had arrived from Hartford. Peggy, Anne's sister, and her family were relaxing in the living room with the Cartwrights as David's Impala swung into the driveway fifteen minutes late. Mandy, who'd been waiting at the door, ran out to the car as he stepped out. "It's been a long time," said David after they'd

42

kissed and held each other. "Let's take a drive up to the bluff."

"Okay, lover," she smiled. "It's so good to see you."

They drove out onto the bluff at Falmouth Heights and parked overlooking Tecumseh's eighth green and the few dim lights of Martha's Vineyard in the distance. Nantucket, off to their left, was barely visible as a low, dark bulge rising out of the water. David adjusted the seat for more leg room, opened his window some three inches, then reached into his jacket pocket for a pack of cigarettes. He lit one, inhaled deeply and blew the smoke out the window. Mandy turned sideways, her left knee against the back of the seat and her hands on her ankle. She cocked her head and smiled at him. "When did you start to smoke?"

"Oh, about a month ago, I guess. Helps you study, you know."

"Sure."

"You look great, Mandy," he said, looking at her.

"You too, David," she replied, reaching over to put her arms around his neck. She really wanted him to touch her. She moved closer to kiss him, but he pulled away.

"Let me butt this thing first," he said.

Mandy sensed something in his voice. "David, what's wrong?"

He took her hand in his and squeezed it, trying to smile. Mandy suddenly grew nervous with his silence.

"I've been trying to think of a way to tell you this, Mandy. Believe me, I don't want to hurt you..."

Mandy sat rigid, afraid of what was coming next.

He paused. "There's this girl in Boston..."

She couldn't hear any more. Mandy pushed open the door and went away from the car to stand at the edge of the bluff. How could he do this, especially now when I need him so much, was all she could think of. She wanted just to disappear, to vanish into the air. Woodenly, she crossed her arms over her chest and looked off into the darkness, a sudden, fearful emptiness in her stomach. Tears flowed over her cheeks. She heard David's door close and the crunch of gravel as he walked toward her. David caught her arm.

"Mandy..."

"You've found someone else," she said in a low voice.

"I didn't plan for it to happen," he confessed. "It just did."

He knew this wouldn't be easy. Mandy just stared off into the darkness, trying to find words. But the pain of rejection, of losing the one she loved so much, for so long, left such an emptiness. Thoughts flew into her mind. She'd been so foolish not to have considered the possibility of David's finding someone else. Surely she could have done something to prevent it. If she hadn't been so caught up with college life at Farmington! If only she hadn't decided to leave him for school. But what choice did she have?

She put her hands to her face and wept. "Why didn't you tell me about this before?"

David stumbled over his words. "I'm sorry, Mandy," he mumbled. "I really am. I didn't want it to happen. It just did. I didn't want to hurt you, and I thought the least I could do was to see you again, to try to explain face to face."

Mandy looked at him and saw the genuine caring in his eyes. But she saw too that he'd changed. He wasn't her David any more. Then it occurred to her that she was alone, and she hated the thought. She longed to hug him and somehow go back to the safety and security they had known. But they stood apart.

A gust of cold wind caught them both, and Mandy suddenly felt chilled to the bone. She started to shiver.

"I think we'd better be going," David said weakly. "It's starting to get cold."

Mandy nodded as she walked in silence back to the car. Neither spoke as David drove back toward Falmouth. She gazed out the window, seeing nothing, feeling only a great emptiness and sensing that somehow she didn't belong here any more.

She barely felt his gentle kiss on her cheek as he said, "Goodnight, Mandy."

"Goodbye, David. I love you," she whispered, turning to open the door.

As she entered the house Mandy tried to hide her grief, tried to compose herself. Everyone was still visiting in the living room, so she stopped briefly at the door with her hand on her forehead, shading her eyes, and complained of a headache. Then she went upstairs and immediately to bed. She couldn't sleep and just lay there, wondering whether she was more upset because he'd rejected her or because she'd lost his love. Had she really loved him at all? Did she really know what love was, after all? Mandy cried herself to sleep that Thanksgiving evening, unsure of the exact source of her hurt.

She awoke the next morning with a dull headache and puffy eyes to the familiar, delicious smell of cooking bacon. Anne appeared at her door. "Good morning, dear..." She stopped short, realizing something was wrong.

"Mandy, what is it, honey?" she asked. "Did you have a fight with David last night?"

Still numb, Mandy tearfully blurted out the details of the past evening, with her mother listening and trying to console her.

"I was going to surprise you with breakfast in bed this morning—pancakes, bacon and juice. How would you like that?" she asked, hoping to make her daughter feel better.

Mandy wasn't hungry. Anne seemed to understand. She gave Mandy a hug and left her alone again. Fortunately, Peggy's family left that morning, and when Mandy finally went downstairs around one in the afternoon, it was apparent that Anne had told Ralph and Brad what had happened. Both were trying their best, rather awkwardly, to be cheerfully nonchalant. Brad was actually considerate for a change. Anne and Mandy decided to go shopping for a few new things for school—"To cheer things up," Anne discreetly whispered to the men—and the family later had a quiet dinner together and an evening in front of the TV. On Saturday Mandy helped Anne around the house and pressed some clothes for school, after which she packed slowly and carefully for her departure the next morning.

Anne and Ralph drove Mandy in to Boston to catch the bus for Farmington. Brad stayed home. He'd complained of a stomach-ache, but Mandy knew he'd had enough moodiness for one weekend and simply didn't want to have to deal with it. The folks chatted on with questions about classes and what she had to do when she returned to Farmington, trying to pull Mandy out of her melancholy. Mandy knew what she was going to do. Almost as self-inflicted punishment she vowed she would have no more fun. She would concentrate all her efforts on studying.

As she kissed her parents at the Trailways depot she smiled

and said, "I love you both so much, and I'm going to make you so proud of me." With that she hopped up the bus steps and waved goodbye.

Chapter Six

Mandy had surprisingly little trouble living up to her resolve to restrict her partying at Farmington. She had less success trying not to think of David and her hurt, partly because she now felt alone, without anyone to lean on. So in the short two and a half weeks between Thanksgiving and the long Christmas break she spent more time in the library than in all the previous weeks combined. And whereas her roommates considered this period one of "academic grace"—just the short lull before the next major holiday and thus to be enjoyed fully—Mandy attended every class session and worked far into the night, drawing complaints from Joanne about the light. Mandy wasn't about to be thwarted; she bought a small, high-intensity reading lamp from the bookstore and went on studying.

She allowed herself one Friday evening dinner-dance party at the Delta Sigma Phi house, a special pre-Christmas occasion considered an honor to attend among the girls of Craig Hall. Stan Baker, the fraternity vice-president, actually stood one evening on the lawn outside her second-story Craig Hall window with three Delta Sig pledges to serenade her before asking her to attend. She couldn't believe it. How could she refuse?

It was a wonderful five-course, formal chicken cordon bleu dinner complete with Dom Perignon champagne and a four-piece string chamber ensemble to entertain them. Later the whole party, some sixty-four in number, went downstairs to the huge basement which had been decorated to resemble an intimate night club. Pledges tended bar and served table as the thirty-two members and their dates danced the evening away to the lively music of Katie and the Leading Edge, a local group that entertained in night clubs in southern Maine and New Hampshire.

At two in the morning Stan drove Mandy, by then considerably tipsy, back to Craig Hall. On the way he stopped the car, turned to her and slowly ran his fingers down her cheek and neck, over her breast and to the crease of her upper thigh, where he kept his hand. Offended, Mandy tried to push his hand away, but she kept slipping off his wrist. Stan, now smiling, offered to take care of her for the night at a friend's apartment, whereupon she opened the car door and vomited on the curb. Taking his handkerchief, she managed a weak "No thanks; take me home," and he drove her the rest of the way without comment.

Lying in bed, the room spinning slowly, she vowed to limit her alcoholic intake and somehow try to learn more about boys.

Following a vicious hangover on Saturday, she buckled down again on Sunday with her studies.

On her next three tests Mandy was rewarded for her conscientious study with two A's and a B, which thrilled her to death. She'd learned that to succeed in college really took a lot of hard work, and if she concentrated, she could do it. She did have a brain after all! For the week before Christmas break she floated on air. She really would make her parents proud of her, and she felt good about herself for the first time that she could remember.

Mandy was so excited about going home Christmas break that she packed everything but her cosmetics two days early. With one remaining test, the biology final, she studied propped up on her bed with the big lamp on, as Joanne was out on a date. When she arrived at eleven o'clock, Mandy went to the desk and continued for another two hours under the reading lamp, finally going to bed at one, tired but ready, she believed. The next day she had to struggle through the final exam, but felt she'd at least made a B-minus or C at worst. And considering it was biology, she was more than pleased. So her courses were finished, and her overall performance, though terrible in the first half of the term, might even be almost respectable by now. She was ready for Christmas break. That last evening she went out with all the girls of 252 to Al's Grape and Grain and had a great time, exchanging gifts and singing Christmas carols over mulled wine. She hardly thought of David.

The big Trailways bus, surprisingly, was more than half full even at 5:45 in the morning. Mandy luckily found a window seat at the middle of the bus and leaned her head back, hoping to fall asleep.

She gazed out the window and saw only darkness and a few streetlights as the bus left Farmington. Then just darkness. She closed her eyes and dozed off. The bus lurched slightly as the driver announced, "Portland! Twenty minutes." It rolled to a standstill in front of the depot, and passengers hurriedly disembarked for a quick breakfast and rest stop. Mandy quickly ate her distasteful, underdone scrambled eggs, leaving one of the greasy sausages and a piece of dried toast. She gulped her grapefruit juice, paid for the meal, took a quick trip to the bathroom and reboarded the bus. She was pleased to have thought to place her overnight bag on her window seat. This time the bus was almost full. She had just seated herself when a young, blond-haired man with a small leather suitcase stopped at her seat and smiled.

"Mind if I sit here next to you?" he asked.

Brent Cutler was a senior pre-law student at Bowdoin College in Brunswick, twenty miles northeast of Portland. He was going home for Christmas to Braintree, Massachusetts, a southern suburb of Boston. He spoke easily with Mandy. He was taking the bus, he explained, because a drunken driver had crumpled a fender on his car in Boston over Thanksgiving holiday; he would pick it up during the break. Mandy thought Brent was gorgeous. He instantly dazzled her with his clean, good looks and charming way. Confidence seemed to ooze from him, she thought. He spoke familiarly of Miami Beach, London and Paris, as easily as he did of Boston. She hung on his every word. Never had she met anyone her age who'd traveled so much— or who seemed to gain her confidence so quickly. He appeared so sincere about everything, and his laugh was so genuine, so rich and infectious. Clearly, Brent was attracted to Mandy, and she couldn't help but be bowled over by him.

As long as they were both going sort of near Boston, he suggested, perhaps they could get together some time over the holidays. He'd be happy to drive down to Falmouth... Mandy happened to mention the Christmas dance at Tecumseh Country Club coming up the next week, and Brent jumped at the chance to be with her. They exchanged addresses and phone numbers, and too soon for Mandy the bus arrived in Boston, where he got off. Mandy watched from the window as he hailed a cab. He smiled broadly and waved before he climbed in and was soon lost in the noisy traffic. Mandy was convinced that this must be God's reward for all her hard work.

Back in Falmouth Mandy asked Ellen about David but didn't try to talk to him. He had left Thayer, having found business college "a drag," and decided to work with his father in Warren's. He'd also taken up with a girl not from Thayer at all but from Falmouth High, whom Mandy knew only by name. Evidently she didn't have aspirations for life beyond Falmouth, and word had it that she didn't require a condom. Mandy was both sad and happy for him, but she realized she didn't really love him as she might have.

After long thought she'd discovered that with David she'd simply enjoyed not having to worry about being alone—more than anything, he had been simply a comfortable means of security for her. Brent, on the other hand, was exciting—and terribly impressive. On Friday evening he pulled into the driveway with his very sporty green MG-B, shining brightly. "The whole thing had to be painted," he explained. Dressed in a charcoal Hart, Schaffner and Marx suit, black Florsheim shoes and looking very Ivy League, Brent simply bowled over Ralph and Anne. As the pair drove off for the dance, Ralph just shook his head and let out a whistle. Anne beamed, thinking how wonderful it was to have such a replacement for David.

The young people had a wonderful evening dancing, and Mandy, feeling like a princess, was thrilled to show him off, especially to Rob McPherson. Then on the day of Christmas Eve Brent drove down to the Cape to bring Mandy a gold bracelet with three little hearts on it. "For someone who's taken my heart," he said. Mandy ate up every word, for Brent indeed was stealing her heart. She believed that this could be the love she wanted so much, perhaps even that she could belong in his world.

Before he drove back to Boston that afternoon they sat in the MG overlooking Nantucket Sound for a short while, a cold wind blowing offshore. He leaned over and kissed her ear gently and massaged the back of her neck. He invited her to a New Year's Eve party in Boston, saying he'd like to get to know her better. Mandy immediately said yes. Brent knew a place in town where they could stay. But perhaps it would be best if Mandy were to tell her parents they'd be staying in his parents' home. There would be no reason for

Ralph and Anne to worry, and they wouldn't have to know Brent's parents were going to Europe right after Christmas.

Mandy didn't like to lie to her parents about where she'd be staying, but she just couldn't tell them the truth. She felt guilty because they had no reason to disbelieve her; they trusted her. And they really liked Brent—he was so polite and well-heeled, but they'd never accept that she wanted to sleep with him. Mandy felt almost compelled to do what she wanted just now; after all, she was in college and should be in charge of her own life. She was mature and should make her own decisions. Besides, she felt so safe with Brent. Everything would be all right, she hoped as she packed the tweed skirt and the creme angora sweater, then laid the graduation pearls on top. They would be just right for the Boston crowd, she guessed, throwing in a pair of jeans and another sweater on the other side of the suitcase, for tomorrow. It hadn't really snowed yet this season except in the hills north and west, but it certainly was cold enough. Then she remembered, winter had just begun a few days ago.

In the dark of late afternoon the couple drove northward along the coast highway. Everything seemed new and fresh. They passed Plymouth, and Mandy knew where the Miles Standish monument and the John Alden house would be, but she thought of them in a different light today. Even the region's history was new to her just now. Then came Braintree, Brent's home town, and Quincy, where John Adams lived. One day Brent will be just as famous, Mandy thought. Every once in a while Brent laid his hand on hers and gave a little squeeze. His hands were so strong and yet gentle, she thought. They seemed to follow every lead from her touch. It felt wonderful. She'd never felt like this with anyone before.

Brent swung into downtown Boston so Mandy could see the Christmas lights. People all over New England made special trips just to see them, and especially the remarkable window displays in Jordan Marsh and Filene's and the other large department stores. Children's eyes just popped out at the fabulous mechanical wonders there, and this evening Mandy and Brent were as little children as they double-parked and stared into the windows and laughed and shook their heads at the marvels before them. For them this evening, Santa Claus was alive indeed.

They stopped at Durgin Park for dinner, just to be insulted by the waiters and enjoy the most famous steak in Boston, then, stuffed and incredibly happy, they wound over to Beacon Hill for the party at the apartment of one of Brent's friends. They were a bit late arriving.

The door opened on a noisy gathering of forty to fifty college-age people dressed in everything from tuxedos and evening gowns to sportcoats and jeans. Most were dressed somewhat fancier than Mandy had expected, and she was therefore a bit self-conscious, but Brent did his best to relax her mind. Music pulsated from speakers placed around the rooms and small groups engaged in casual, laughing conversation while others wandered around snacking hors d'oeuvres and sipping cocktails. Food and drink were plentiful and a huge punchbowl, containing a pink champagne concoction, sat in the middle of a table. Brent fixed screwdrivers for Mandy and himself. Julie's sister had advised her several years ago that a screwdriver was a safe drink.

Nevertheless, after some time Mandy started to feel the influence of the drinks and began to lean on Brent, to rely on his judgment, but he seemed so much in control of the situation that it didn't really matter. And when he smiled that beautiful smile and pulled her to himself with his arm around her waist, she felt so secure, so safe.

After a short while someone mentioned to Brent that a small crowd was going to slip out to the night club at the Prudential Tower to ring in the New Year. Brent conveniently happened to have a fake identification card for Mandy. "I had it made just for you, for just such an occasion," he explained, smiling, as he gave her a hug. Without a thought of how he could arrange such a thing, she took it.

What a view from the top. It was like being above a fairy-tale kingdom of lights. The band played wonderfully, in a way that Mandy had never heard "live" before. She and Brent whirled around the dance floor between several Brandy Alexanders, which she had on his recommendation. Then at the stroke of midnight Brent pulled her to him and kissed her with such feeling that Mandy thought she'd melt. His whole body beckoned, and then he whispered, "Let's go."

They moved through the crowd of boisterous merrymakers and out to the elevator. Mandy hung onto his arm, knowing he was in charge. He knew best. Outside, they held their coats tightly around them against the wintry blast, and Mandy clung to Brent as they struggled to the car, heads down against the bitter wind. He drove a short distance to a quiet apartment overlooking the Charles River.

Mandy leaned against the mantlepiece as the fire began to blaze, and she started to feel warm and relaxed. The drinks, the evening's excitement, and Brent's knowing hands had left her vulnerable. Brent brought two small glasses of a creme liqueur. Still standing before the fire, they toasted both the New Year and the evening they were about to begin. Brent slowly undressed Mandy and himself, then he took her into the bedroom. They made love slowly and passionately, long into the wee hours. There was no thought of tomorrow. When Mandy awoke, she knew this was the real thing. She was deeply in love with Brent. In the morning they showered together, soaping each other thoroughly and sensuously, enjoying each other's body immensely. Later they cooked ham and eggs with English muffins. Breakfast had never tasted so wonderful. But too soon they had to leave for Falmouth again. College resumed in only three days, and Mandy's parents had planned a day-long family ski trip to Laconia, New Hampshire, before driving her back across the border to Farmington.

The ride back was painful for Mandy; somehow there was a difference from the previous night's mood. There were so many things she wanted to talk about, but Brent seemed somewhat preoccupied and tended not to hear what she was saying at times. And he drove the little MG considerably faster than the speed limit. "You may be on the quarter system, with your finals all done, but Bowdoin's still on semesters, and I've got finals coming up. I've got to get back to Braintree to get some studying done," he explained.

Mandy didn't like to see this special time end this way. They needed to talk more. Last night was the most wonderful night of her life, and yet she somehow felt so empty. Maybe it was all a dream. Well, she thought, there'll be lots of times for talk together. And Bowdoin is really pretty close to Farmington, less than an hour's drive...

When they kissed goodbye outside the house in Falmouth, Brent smiled and promised to call her when he returned to Bowdoin.

They hugged tightly, he kissed her again, then he jumped into the MG and roared out of the driveway, waving his arm. "I'll call," he yelled. He honked once as the car rounded the corner, and he was gone.

Chapter Seven

When Mandy returned to Craig Hall, she was shocked to find that only Barbara Connors remained of her three roommates. Joanne and Linda had flunked out, and they had removed their belongings. Mandy almost cried when it occurred to her that she hadn't even written down their home addresses or phone numbers. Sadly, Mandy remembered sitting in the auditorium with all the other incoming students that first day of orientation last semester, when the college president had stood at the podium and announced, "Look at the person at your left and the person on your right. At the end of the first year only one of the three of you will still be here. You'll have to work to stay in college." Well, Mandy reflected, at least Barbara and I are still here. Barely. She renewed her resolve to limit the fun and work hard at her studies, to make her parents proud of her.

Two other girls, both mid-term high school graduates from central Maine, replaced the two former roommates. Mandy promised herself she wouldn't become too friendly with the girls—not only might they become distractions to her work, but they too might flunk out, and she didn't want to lose any more good friends. It hurt too much.

She and Barbara tried to make the new girls feel welcome, but somehow her heart wasn't in it. Nevertheless, as old hands more or less, they showed the girls something of the ropes around the dorm and saw them through the rigmarole of registration. Because the oldtimers had been able to register before the semester ended, they now had only to start attending classes. Mandy's courses included carrying over to the second semester in English, French and biology, but half of her courses were new—psychology, sociology and indoor team sports which would change at midterm to intermediate tennis, her favorite sport. She knew she could count on at least one A.

After what seemed an eternity—three days after Mandy

arrived back at Farmington—Brent called. He was gearing up for his final semester at Bowdoin and had received some bad news from the registrar. He apparently had to make up two extra courses in order to graduate, having got unsatisfactory grades in them earlier. If he was going to law school, he simply had to do well this semester. His workload, therefore, would be monumental and he wouldn't be able to take as much time off to see her as he'd hoped. But he'd call whenever he had the chance. He wished her well for the start of the semester and told her he missed her a lot. She loved him and needed to be with him, but his first priority was to graduate. She understood that his needs overruled hers, and as long as he could make the grade, she was happy for him. When she hung up, she was in tears.

For her part, Mandy stuck to her resolve, attending classes faithfully and studying diligently, though she missed Brent terribly. She realized it was silly. She'd seen him only four times—on the bus to Boston, twice briefly in Falmouth, and their fabulous time at New Year's. But she loved him so much. Somehow she'd just have to work harder to keep from going crazy with desire to be with him.

January passed with Mandy's taking off only once for a ski break with four Craig girls at Titcomb Slope, a few miles north of town. Winter had finally hit western Maine in the form of a snowstorm that swept out of Ontario and Quebec into northern New England. She couldn't resist the call of the slopes on that third Saturday of the month. Unfortunately, it seemed that the entire population of Farmington and half that of the college showed up as well. The other half had no doubt gone off to Tater Mountain in the west. The girls had to cut their day short when one of their party fractured an ankle during a hard fall and had to be taken back to the college and then to the hospital in Skowhegan. But at least Mandy had had a lot of fun and some good exercise and best of all, a time away from the books.

The skiing had also taken her mind off another small problem that was beginning to gnaw at her. She had been late for her period almost a week now and had hoped the exercise might have brought it on. No such luck. Mandy could never set her watch by her periods, but she'd never been more than a week late, either. Well, perhaps tomorrow—or at least by the next day. Tomorrow came and went, and the next day, and the next, and still nothing happened. Mandy became increasingly worried. She had difficulty concentrating in class and still greater trouble studying later in the evenings. Her mind wandered from the pages to possibilities of pregnancy, of what she might have to tell Brent and her parents. She could never tell her parents! What would they think? They'd be crushed. She'd disappointed them so many times in the past; she simply couldn't disappoint them again. They'd sacrificed so much for her. She wondered whether or not she should call Brent. He hadn't called....

Suddenly Mandy woke up to the fact that she'd been used. Falling for Brent had been a great mistake, a fantasy of her own making, and now it appeared she might have to suffer the consequences alone. What a fool she'd been. Clearly, he'd never felt the same for her as she'd felt about him, especially after their night together on New Year's Eve.

As each day passed, the certainty that she was pregnant became more and more apparent. Maybe she should go see the doctor at the student health center. He could tell her for sure. But what if she really were pregnant? Would he tell her parents? She couldn't risk it. Besides, maybe the period will start tomorrow. She tried to put it out of her mind, but it wouldn't go away. She weighed herself every day and was happy at least to see that her weight was slowly going down and not up. It never occurred to her that it was because she wasn't eating as she should.

Another month passed. Still there was no period. Mandy felt no different inside and she wasn't gaining weight. She couldn't be pregnant. Perhaps she just skipped a month. It was known to happen. She tried her best not to think about it, but the prospect of pregnancy was constantly before her, and she had no answers, no one to turn to. Only Brent could help, and she couldn't trouble him. She would tough it out, wait for her period. It just had to start. There was no alternative but to wait.

When March came and there was still no sign of a period, Mandy resigned herself to the fact that she was pregnant. Alone in her room early one afternoon she stood naked in front of the mirror, staring at herself. Her eyes glistened with tears. Her life was suddenly so complex. Where could she turn? Whom could she trust? There was only Brent, and she hadn't heard from him except for the one call at the start of the semester. He hadn't tried to see her at all. The room seemed cold, and goosebumps appeared on her flesh. She was so alone, so frightened and ashamed. She wondered if anyone could notice what was happening to her. This was a thousand times worse than first feeling the scar on the back of her head. And she thought that was so terrible.

Mandy gazed blankly at her body in the mirror. Never had she been more discouraged with the way it looked. She placed her hands on her abdomen and gently pressed inward. She slid her hands over the fullness of her middle and up past her ribs, to her breasts. Her eyes rested there and she wondered if they too would grow. She longed to go back six months in her life. It all could have been so different. This was supposed to be the best time in my life, she thought. But now, she concluded, it's the worst.

Mandy finally called Brent at the end of the first week of March. He wasn't there, so she left a message for him to call her. Two days later, he finally called.

"Holy shit! That's all I need," he complained. "Are you absolutely sure you're knocked up?"

"Well, not absolutely sure, but pretty sure," she said. "This hasn't ever happened before."

"I'll tell you what," he replied. "You go down to the health center and check it out to make sure, and then we'll see."

Through her sobbing she tried to listen as he told her not to worry, that he would take care of everything. She should leave everything to him, and he'd call her back in two or three days. He promised. But in the meantime she should go see a doctor and really confirm that she was pregnant. It would be senseless to go through an elaborate plan unless she knew for sure.

Mandy dutifully went to the health center and asked the nurse if parents had to be notified if one of the students was found to be pregnant. She was greatly relieved when the nurse said no, and so she requested an examination. It turned out positive; she was pregnant.

Claiming she was ill, Mandy stayed in her room for a day and a half, going down only for quick meals and then back upstairs. She had to be by herself. Finally she called Brent again. Much to her surprise, he was entirely civil, and told her he'd solved the problem. He'd pick her up early on Saturday morning and they would drive to Boston, where she would have an abortion. Everything was arranged. There would be no difficulty and everything would be fine. She should leave all the details to him. They'd stay together in a motel for the night and return to Maine on Sunday and resume classes the next day. Just as if nothing had ever happened. What more could she ask?

Sensing that she was trapped and had no choice, Mandy reluctantly agreed to Brent's plan.

Chapter Eight

Brent arrived at seven-thirty on Saturday morning outside Craig Hall. Mandy, already waiting in the lobby, saw him drive up. She ran out to the car and he whisked her away, mumbling that he was glad to see her but wished the circumstances were different. They were curiously silent on the road. He asked her how she was feeling, and she wondered how his studies were going. Otherwise they seemed at a loss for words and simply listened to the radio. Neither one seemed to know how to put feelings into words. She occasionally reached over to touch his hand and tried the occasional smile, but he pretended to be preoccupied with driving and they made little other contact. As the miles passed Mandy perceived that Brent seemed cold, aloof. He hadn't asked about breakfast or whether she might need to stop for anything. Whenever he did say anything, it tended to be abrupt, business-like, and Mandy started to feel that he was largely insensitive to her feelings, that he was concerned only for himself, certainly not for her. There were long stretches of dead silence between them, with only music from WHEB to interrupt the quiet. The green MG raced down the highway.

Thoughts raced through Mandy's mind. Was this what she was supposed to do? What else could she do? She loved her family too much to have them share the shame, the pain. She felt so helpless, so ashamed, so terrified. And she sensed that this man sitting beside her was concerned only with his own hide, that he really didn't love her, that he'd only used her for a brief interlude during a holiday. Was the story of his additional graduation requirements simply a lie, just a way to get her off his back? Was she worth nothing more to him than just a potential paternity suit? Something to diminish his proper Bostonian reputation? Somehow she couldn't put her thoughts into words, couldn't bring herself to confront him, but deep down she sensed their truth. She'd trusted Brent, and he'd proved untrustworthy. Now she had to trust him again, but she didn't believe she could trust anybody at the moment. She'd thought she really, truly loved him, and the pain of her realizations ate through to her soul. She now knew her emotions had really fooled her, that she didn't want to be with him for the rest of her life, and she wasn't entirely sure she even wanted to be with him for the weekend. For the moment, however, there was no choice. She was angry at herself for her stupidity, ashamed of the whole sordid mess and becoming increasingly frightened.

They drove without stopping into the city, to a seedy section of old tenement flats that was unfamiliar to Mandy. The scene just made her feel worse. Dirty brick tenements lined the streets, and garbage lay piled on the corners. Men stood there as well, leaning against broken garage doors, staring at nothing, passing the time. Brent stopped at a corner and quickly reached into the glove compartment for a map that was folded open to this part of town. He quickly moved on as he grabbed it. He made a few turns, went down a long, straight street and made another turn. The tenements ended, replaced by tall, narrow old houses scarcely three feet apart, with peeling, painted clapboards or sided with tarpaper of dark, indeterminate colors. Debris littered the gutters and papers blew across the street. At an intersection Brent looked again at the map and said, "This is it. Look for Jersey Way half way down the block, 2935-C." Mandy felt her skin start to crawl.

On the opposite corner a small crowd of men lazed around outside a bar, several clasping brown paper bags evidently containing bottles of liquor. "Mac's Tavern," read the sign, swinging back and forth in the breeze. Two men sauntered away from their group as the green MG moved across the intersection. Mandy sensed that they knew what Brent was looking for, why the couple was here, and they continued slowly down the sidewalk as he took a left into Jersey Way. The men followed and stood at the end of the narrow roadway and watched as Brent found 2935 and stopped the car.

Jersey Way was little more than an alley between blocks, and ramshackle garages backed right up to the roadway, but mailboxes lined the drive and tiny porches, against the doorways, looked out onto the alleyway and the miniature plots of dirt that once grew grass. Open stairways, precariously attached to the backs of the houses, marched up to the second and third stories, to rickety landings with a chair or two on them. Laundry, strung out on wires from houses to telephone poles, fluttered in the breeze.

"Stay in the car, keep the windows up and lock the doors," Brent said. He got out and went up to the little porch and knocked on the door. Mandy sat scared to death, feeling cold and clammy, almost hypnotized by the scene around her. She noticed two fat women leaning over the railing from their chairs from one of the upper landings across the way. They were staring down at her. Another was hanging laundry out and occasionally she too would glance down at the car. They know why we're here, she realized. My God, hurry up, Brent. She reached up for the rear-view mirror and adjusted it to see out the rear window and saw the two men still standing at the end of the alley. Mandy had never been so scared in her life.

Shortly afterward, Brent came out to the car again. Mandy opened his door and he reached into the glove compartment and grabbed an envelope. Then he felt under the seat and took out a pistol, which he shoved into his belt under his jacket. Shocked, Mandy just stared at him, too frightened even to ask what was happening. Brent seemed cold, distant, and she knew he must be frightened as well. It was as if someone had given him precise instructions on the procedure; she wondered if the gun were part of those. "Let's go," he said. "Lock your door."

They walked up to the door where a man, near sixty, thin and wearing a red plaid shirt, met them. He ushered them up a flight of stairs to a flat and took them inside. There a woman in a faded apron over her housedress took Mandy's hand and showed her into the kitchen. The man told Brent he could wait downstairs.

They both went out, leaving Mandy with the woman. The thought skitted through Mandy's mind that this must be where he pays for this thing.

Then she suddenly thought of her mother. How horrified she would be if she knew.

The woman smiled at Mandy and tried to put her at ease. She explained that she was a registered nurse, that she did this all the time and there was nothing to worry about. To reassure Mandy, the woman took her to the sideboard and pointed out pictures of her children and grandchildren. Mandy should just think of her as a caring, grandmotherly person who had loads of experience in these things and who wouldn't harm a flea. She smiled and put her arms around Mandy, sensing her fright. Then the woman told Mandy the gist of what she would do. But everything would be all right; she should just try to relax. Why, heavens, before she knew, it would all be over and everything would be back to normal. It was only weeks later that Mandy realized the woman didn't ever show her any diplomas or medical certificates of any kind.

Tears welled up in Mandy's eyes, and she started to cry. The woman asked, "Are you sure you really want to go through with this, dear?"

So many confused and contradictory feelings were flooding Mandy's mind that she couldn't give an answer. She certainly didn't want to do this, but there wasn't any choice! She couldn't have this baby, but she was taking its life, and that was just as bad. Her head may have nodded slightly. The woman put her arm around Mandy's shoulder and guided her through the cramped and stuffy bedroom to the bathroom, telling her again not to worry, but just to take her clothes off and put on the surgical gown there on the toilet seat.

Mandy followed her instructions and went into the bathroom. Though the apartment was quite old and these people clearly were not prosperous, the bathroom wasn't as clean as Mandy thought it should be, and she didn't want to touch anything. She felt dirty, humiliated, and she wished this was not happening. Her mind began almost to float out of the room, out of the apartment. She felt that if she wished hard enough, she might be somewhere else just now. When she came out of the bathroom everything in the apartment seemed to blur into everything else—she couldn't tell whether she was in the bedroom or dining room or kitchen. Or were they simply all parts of one big room? But it didn't matter now. She wanted so much to be away from there.

The woman, who seemed far off to Mandy, touched her arm and told her to lie on the table. It might have been in the kitchen or perhaps the dining room, but it was all right anyway. There was a thick pad on top but it was flat and hard and very uncomfortable. Mandy lay back and shut her eyes tightly. A voice from far away said something like "the same thing as having your first pelvic, ...just irritate the uterus." Vaguely remembering the physical she had to have before going off to college, Mandy felt terribly cold and pretended she couldn't feel anything that had to be done, as long as it were done as quickly as possible. She kept her eyes closed and prayed frantically, more thoughts than words. She needed to be protected from this thing, to be forgiven for being such an awful person, for taking this life within her.

Mandy gripped the sides of the table, knees up and spread, her eyes shut, praying for her parents, for her life and this other little life. She felt something cold and hard probing deep within her, and then a sharp cramping pain that made her clench her fists and brought her head up from the table with a cry. Was it five seconds or five minutes? Then a dull, hard ache spread through her middle and stayed. Lying there, she turned her head to the side and wept.

The woman was talking. She was saying that Mandy would feel something like menstrual cramps for a while, that they would get more severe after some time, and she should go somewhere and rest. But for the moment she should just lie there for a little while; she could get up shortly. It was all finished.

"Do you feel well enough to stand?" The question came from a distance, but the woman stood next to Mandy, a hand on her shoulder. Mandy didn't care how she felt. Still weeping, with an effort she pushed herself up from the table and eased herself off onto the floor. She walked unsteadily toward the bathroom and tried to dress quickly, still feeling a hard ache in the middle of her body. She felt cold, alone and frightened, and the tears wouldn't stop.

When she came out into the room, the woman handed her a paper bag, saying, "You'll need these. You'll see what looks like old blood, and in a couple of hours you'll abort. There'll be a tiny thing that looks like a sac and you'll bleed a little for some time, and then things will be back to normal." The woman smiled.

At that moment Brent came into the room. "How do you feel?" he asked.

"I don't know. Not so good. Let's just go," she whispered.

Mandy walked gingerly down the steps and out to the car, with Brent beside her. She was still very afraid from the "operation" and this terrible neighborhood, too frightened even to try to remember what the woman had instructed her to expect and do. And she felt angry at herself and Brent. She knew she'd gotten into this pickle by herself, but Brent had certainly manipulated her as well. He'd just wanted to get her into bed—and just for that stupid holiday. And he'd been so cold toward her. Even this gesture was to save himself. She knew she had to be with him now, but she wanted only to run away and be by herself. Well, it wouldn't be long before they'd be apart, and she couldn't wait. If only it weren't for this driving ache in her lower stomach.

Brent had arranged a motel room for the weekend. They drove for some twenty minutes before pulling up to a Howard Johnson's. Mandy stayed in the car, eyes closed and head back on the seat, while he checked in. What was it the lady had told her to watch for? A dull pain in her lower back and spasmodic cramps began, and she became frightened again. Was this supposed to be happening? Brent had been terribly nervous driving from the house to the motel, and that had made her all the more uncomfortable. She couldn't relax and sitting became more unpleasant by the minute.

He returned, climbed in and swung the car around toward the back of the motel and pulled into a parking spot. "Here we are." Thank God it's at least on the first floor, Mandy thought gratefully. Her cramps worsening, she immediately undressed and got into bed while he brought in the luggage.

She laid back on the bed and clutched her stomach, and for the first time Brent realized that Mandy was really in pain, and it wouldn't go away. He made some effort to comfort her, but she just silently wished him gone. Besides, his presence somehow just aggravated the hurt. She was stuck in Boston in a strange room, away from her bed at college, away from her home and parents, alone even with this person. How she wanted to be home! But she couldn't go home, not before she did this thing first. She vaguely reflected that Boston was the scene of the single most wonderful time in her love life, and now it was the place of her worst experience. Through the pain she almost laughed. Well, she deserved what she was getting; it was her own fault. She hated herself even more than she hated Brent.

It wasn't long before Brent said, "You know, we haven't had anything to eat yet. What do you say we have something brought over from the restaurant? We've got room service."

As he spoke, Mandy remembered he didn't even have the courtesy to ask if she'd had breakfast. She hadn't; her anxiety was too great to eat so early. And they certainly hadn't had lunch. But Mandy's aching abdomen overwhelmed her hunger pangs, and she simply wished both would go away. Or maybe she should just die and get it over with. That would be simpler for everyone. But she didn't want to die, and she knew she needed food for her strength.

The prospect of being here with Brent for twenty-four unbroken hours appalled her, but she couldn't tell him that. She just wanted to be alone—this was such a private matter. Then it occurred to her that here was a chance for some privacy.

"I really can't stand Howard Johnson's food," she lied. "Maybe you could find a Kentucky Fried Chicken place nearby. I'd really love some of that. Why don't you see if you can find one?"

She rolled over onto her stomach, trying to ease the gnawing pain.

"Shit, Mandy," Brent protested. "Howard Johnson's has all kinds of stuff right here. That's why I picked this place. It can't be all that bad."

Mandy looked up at him with a pained look on her face, which he recognized as genuine.

"Please?"

"Well, hell's bells and balls of fire. If you insist," he growled. "Let me check the fucking phone book."

Brent left to find the chicken house. It was good to have the privacy, but her cramps worsened; they came in hard waves, just like birth contractions. And the bleeding had started. Brent was such a stranger to her; it was hard to envision the intimacy they'd shared. This was so awkward with him here. She wished he would go, but she needed him in case something went wrong.

The bleeding worsened, which worried Mandy, but then it stopped altogether. She realized the woman hadn't told her exactly what would happen, hadn't really described what she should expect, and she couldn't remember what she'd said anyway. How long would this take? How much bleeding is there supposed to be? Why is there just this bright red blood and not the "old" blood that I'm supposed to see? Why doesn't this awful pain go away? How long is it supposed to last? Mandy became increasingly confused and frightened as time went on and the sharp pains continued.

She'd had forty minutes to herself while Brent went off for the food. He returned with a large bucket of chicken, a warm loaf of bread, mashed potatoes and gravy, cole slaw, all in paper cups, and a couple of canned Cokes. Mandy was famished but the usually delicious chicken lacked its appeal for her just then and seemed only greasy. She ate little, forcing down some cole slaw and wishing such restaurants served healthier fare.

Brent wolfed down four pieces of chicken, some potatoes and gravy, almost a third of the bread, and a Coke. Belching loudly and patting himself on the stomach, he stood up and announced that he was still thirsty and wanted to check out the lounge. Was that all right with her? He wouldn't be gone long. Mandy looked at him resignedly. "Why not?" she said.

By the time Brent returned, staggering slightly, slurring his speech and carrying a bag full of beer and snacks, Mandy was in real pain. She'd had to make several trips to the bathroom, each time terrified of what she might have to flush away. She was starting to bleed again and felt a tremendous pressure in the abdomen, which sent her scurrying back under the blankets. She tried to sleep, but Brent kept the light on, preoccupied with his beer and snacks and watching TV. Eventually he fell asleep in front of the set, with the test pattern and the unrelenting hiss irritating her.

Through the night Mandy tried to sleep, but had constantly to get up and struggle to the bathroom because of the bleeding. Things weren't going well at all. The uterus had obviously been irritated—perhaps too much—but there seemed to be nothing but blood. Mandy thought that perhaps she was hemorrhaging but didn't know quite what that was. And she had the grave feeling that the abortion wasn't taking place. My God, she thought, did I go through all that just to bleed to death?

She drifted off to sleep once more, only to be shocked awake by a hand roughly fondling her breast. Brent had wakened and got into bed beside her and was moving close behind her as she lay on her side. She was horrified as she felt his hardness pressing against her buttocks and instantly felt herself struggling with nausea, the stench of stale beer appalling her, his nose and lips against her neck. Mandy pulled away, moaning her great displeasure, but Brent persisted, pulling her closer, tightening his hand around her breast. "Come on, Mandy, I'm horny," he slurred. "It's the least you can do. Come on, I'm paying for this whole thing."

Mandy couldn't believe her ears. She became frightened and revolted at once. Wrenching free from his grasp, she bolted for the bathroom and slammed and locked the door. She spent the rest of the night there, hurt and disgusted.

The evening passed with only Brent getting much sleep. Mandy nodded off occasionally but woke up sharply, worried about her bleeding. But nothing had changed by early morning—the pain and her shame bore heavily on her. The signs the woman had said to look for weren't happening, and Mandy's anxiety grew as the sun rose over Boston Harbor.

To make matters more aggravating, Brent, who apparently didn't remember his late-night advances, started asking, "How long do you think it's going to take? Is it done yet?"

"No, just bleeding," Mandy replied. At one point, irritated, she said, "I'm trying as hard as I can, so stop asking stupid questions."

But he didn't let up and his patience dwindled. He badgered Mandy persistently with, "Is it done yet?" He was like a child on a trip constantly asking how much longer it would take to get where they were going.

She answered "I don't know" so many times that he became angry. He yelled, "Come on, quit fucking around! Let's get this thing done!" and stomped out to the parking lot, slamming the door, which drove her to frustrated tears.

Mandy wished her mother was with her. She needed someone to hold her hand, to comfort her. All she really wanted was to be rid of Brent and have a chance to start over.

By nine in the morning, still nothing had changed. Mandy suddenly felt a strong urge to leave. She began to wash and dress.

Brent asked again if it had happened yet. She could feel his impatience and frustration. She became angry as well and demanded that they leave immediately. There was no reason to stay here imprisoned in this motel. She wanted to go back to school. She didn't have to wait; she just wanted to relieve Brent of his damned obligation, to get away from him. She was uncomfortable here with him any longer. Without hesitation he began getting his things together.

They packed quickly and left. As they drove away from Boston Mandy somehow felt a little better. The cramping wasn't as severe and the twinges of gnawing pain came much further apart. But she didn't tell Brent about the apparent improvement. Several hours later they pulled up in front of Craig Hall. Brent turned to her and, rather coldly, told Mandy that he wanted to be notified when it was finished—after all, he had paid a bundle of money for the weekend. And he felt somewhat cheated because nothing was finalized yet. He clearly wanted to be off the hook. Mandy was disgusted with everything about him, but somehow she couldn't tell him that.

She promised to call him as early as appropriate, knowing in her heart that she never wanted to see or hear from him again. How had she been so foolish to think he cared about anything but his own pleasure and comfort? She loathed him and his deceptions and dearly wanted to get her feelings toward him off her chest as she stood there. But what good would that do? He wouldn't change. Besides, all she really wanted was to be away from him and rest alone in her own bed. How she hoped no one was in the room.

Suddenly Mandy felt comfort in being alone on the sidewalk; she didn't even turn to look as the green MG pulled out onto the street and roared away.

Miraculously, her roommates were gone when Mandy arrived in her room. She tossed her things down and went immediately to the bathroom. Still bleeding, but not as heavily as earlier. She was grateful but still terribly confused and frightened about what to expect—and when this thing would finally be over. She hurriedly unpacked, pushing her clothes into a drawer, undressed and got into bed. She closed her eyes and prayed that everything would soon be over.

The three other roommates trickled back to the dorm by dinner time. The two new girls, who'd found much in common and had become fast friends, tripped down together leaving Barbara alone with the bedridden Mandy. Sensing that something was seriously wrong with her, Barbara offered to bring her supper up to the room. The two ate together from trays, neither saying much—Barbara concerned but not wishing to pry, and Mandy unwilling to admit the truth about her affliction. Afterwards Mandy thanked Barbara for her kindness and made some excuse about her period—heavy bleeding, cramps and a headache—so she could be left to herself. She tried desperately to fall asleep so she could awake the next morning with everything back to normal. But it wasn't to be.

By three in the morning Mandy woke up, in serious trouble. She was hemorrhaging badly. Ever since supper the pains and cramps had melted together and her body began to shudder so much that she could no longer even cry. Somehow, inexplicably, her fear prevented her from crying. The bleeding, she noticed, was constant and heavy. Her trips to the bathroom increased during the evening, and she found it uncomfortable either to lie down or sit. At one point she stood leaning over the bowl to vomit but found she had to sit to expel more fluid, and this caused her to become increasingly panicky. She was convinced she would die.

In desperation, Mandy finally woke up Barbara. All apologies, she stuttered something about having appendicitis and needing help. Could Barbara help her down to the health center? There was no one else she could turn to.

Barbara hadn't been able to sleep well anyway and was quite aware that something was seriously wrong with Mandy, having been awakened several times by her low groaning and the frequent trips to the bathroom—which happened to be just beyond the foot of Barbara's bed. She quickly dressed and helped Mandy into her clothes. Arm in arm they went carefully and quietly down the stairs and out to Barbara's car. Incongruously, Mandy protested weakly that they shouldn't be doing this—they might be caught breaking curfew and sneaking out of the dorm. But Barbara said she'd take care of that little problem, and within minutes they were at health center.

The nurse at the reception desk managed to obtain answers to three or four questions before Mandy collapsed, blacking out completely. The next thing Mandy knew was the sound of her mother's voice coming through a long tunnel, then her father's voice as well. Her eyes opened slowly, and she had to squint under the unaccustomed light. As if in a dream she saw her mother smiling down at her. Was this a dream? How could her parents be there? They were so far away and didn't know what was happening. She brought her hands to her forehead and tried to focus. Sure enough, there they were, speaking together and smiling at their daughter.

Mandy couldn't find words. How could this be? This must be a dream. But it couldn't be—they were here, wherever that was. And they knew! Emotions piled up within her and a fountain of tears erupted. "I'm sorry, I'm sorry, I'm sorry," was all she could say. Her parents reached down and held her, tried to comfort her, and over and over they said that everything was fine now, that it was all over.

Slowly, little by little they told Mandy what had taken place during the operation and while she had slept. And now that she was awake, they were allowed to sit with her and remain while the nurse— and occasionally the doctor—came in to check her from time to time. Finally he told them her condition was improving rapidly. As early as tomorrow she would be going home to rest up. There were only two days before the official start of spring break anyway, so she might as well have a couple of days' head start. She was all right now, but she could use the rest.

Mandy's mother explained that she was very fortunate that she'd been brought in for help when she had, because she'd lost a great deal of blood. Mandy was tremendously relieved. Then it occurred to her that her parents knew there must have been a cause for this terrible physical crisis, and she felt an overwhelming shame for what she'd done and didn't know how to begin to tell them what had happened. Fortunately for her they didn't press for particulars that day. Nor did they on the following day, when they all set off for Falmouth and spring break.

For almost three days at home Mandy was silent, lost in her thoughts as the finality of what she had done sank in and took root. An immense sadness took her over, and she brooded on her self-worth as she paced the beach at Falmouth Heights. Everyone was so nice— and she deserved none of it. Even Bradley seemed more sympathetic than usual. Had mom and dad told him? She hoped not—and was relieved that they hadn't. They'd simply said, "Why, Mandy's just sick and has to rest at home for a few days."

She tried to blank out the nightmare of the past week, but finally her parents confronted her with their concern and hurt. As Mandy began to relive the details of what had happened, Ralph became livid with rage toward Brent, even to the point of shedding tears for his daughter. He wanted to press charges against Brent for causing her near murder. As his anger grew, Mandy became almost hysterical; she envisioned the whole matter exposed to light. If this were to become a court case, she'd have to relive the whole thing over again just for the sake of the lawyers.

It was supposed to have been such a simple solution, and it became so complicated, so ugly. Mandy's mother was gentle and understanding, and she guided her family through the crisis. She understood what Mandy would have to go through if there were a trial, and she knew Ralph well enough to let him release steam up to a point. Then carefully, slowly, she convinced him to simmer down. Mandy had already been through enough terrible experiences for a while and didn't need to go over the whole thing again, particularly when she'd vowed never to see Brent Cutler again.

They knew they had to respect their daughter's wishes in dropping the whole issue. After all, she was well now and there was no permanent damage, the doctors had assured them. And for that they all had to be thankful. Ralph steamed for a while, occasionally losing his temper and ranting about how that son of a bitch shouldn't be able to get away with it, and then he'd calm down again.

Mandy's parents seemed eventually to have reconciled the matter with themselves, but Mandy hadn't. And it would be years before she could. In that year, 1964, abortions were illegal and the subject of much destructive gossip; a family's reputation could be permanently ruined, and in those days a small town could perpetuate a corrosive guilt in anyone who dared try an abortion. She knew she'd have to live with the guilt of taking a tiny life, something that no one had warned her about in any talk she'd heard dealing with the subject of abortion.

She felt a strong need to attend church that weekend, but by

Sunday they would be on the road back to Farmington. Not caring about a specific denomination, she went over to the Congregational church, the closest to the house, and tried the door. Locked. Of course, she thought; no one's here on a Friday evening, even though it's early. She thought to try one more and went over a few blocks to the Catholic church. The door was open, and she walked in, footsteps echoing in the silent expanse of the building, and up to the front pew near the altar, where she sat down.

There in the empty silence of the church, she felt suddenly warm and somehow comforted through her tears. She wanted so much to be forgiven. Perhaps God could forgive her. The Bible spoke in so many places of people being forgiven for lots of killings. Even David, the greatest king of Israel, had committed adultery and murder, and God forgave him. She knew she didn't want Brent's baby, couldn't ever want it—but she hated herself for killing the life inside. She knew it would take a long time before that terrible emptiness would be gone.

No one in Falmouth but Mandy's parents knew about the abortion, and for that she was grateful. She owed her family at least to be spared the shame of small-town gossip. And after a few days they said nothing more about it. Nor did they press her about what her plans were now—she needed time to forget. She was so lucky to have such understanding parents; she'd been a fool not to have confided in them. Mandy was more determined than ever to turn her life around.

Going back to the dorm was uncomfortable at first. She hoped no one knew. But no one asked her where she'd been, except to ask if she'd had a good vacation. Barbara had been wonderfully discreet, never letting on that she knew, and as far as the dorm was concerned, spring break had its memories for everyone.

Chapter Nine

Spring in Farmington was beautiful, wonderful. The snow was gone, birds chirped, plant life turned a marvelous green, leaves and flowers grew, and the air was so clean. On campus, doors and windows stood open to the fresh air, replacing winter staleness. The sound of stereos and transistor radios began to fill the air around the dorms, and some of the men hung their laundry and sometimes themselves on window ledges, where perhaps a young co-ed would notice. This was an invigorating time, but spring fever set in nevertheless. Studies required diligent concentration as the renewed outdoors called persuasively. And the keggers could now resume. For Mandy, this was a time for rededicated study, but it was also tennis season. And her phys-ed class in intermediate tennis had begun.

The class met Tuesdays and Thursdays from three o'clock to four-thirty. Terrible hours, Mandy thought, but she was glad that at least it was her last class of the day. When she'd finished dressing and walked out to the courts, men also were gathering around the instructor, a slim, athletically built woman in her young thirties. Slightly surprised, Mandy hadn't known it would be co-ed. She was a little hesitant, realizing that men would be there, but otherwise she felt good and she shrugged it off. There would be great exercise and some stiff competition to build her game.

For Mandy the hour and a half each day flew by quickly; she felt so good, so much at home on the courts. She'd forgotten how much she missed being outdoors in the fresh air, the warm sun beating down. This was going to be good for her. She felt a bit flabby and easily became winded the first two days at tennis.

The instructor spent her time walking from court to court, giving both group and personal attention to the various players and assessing their abilities. Then at the beginning of the second week, she called the class together and announced that they'd be working for a while on the intricacies of mixed doubles. For that first day she chose four people to demonstrate the basic technique of mixed doubles—serve and volley, where to stand during service, where and how to move so as to protect the court, the technique of poaching, and so on—and every minute or so, with everyone looking on, she would stop the action to demonstrate proper technique. At the end of class she told everyone to be on time Thursday; they'd all get a chance to try it.

Mandy knew the basic strategies of doubles. In fact, she'd played on the Falmouth High team and at Tecumseh had taught the youngsters the very same techniques. But playing with people you weren't used to was another story.

The instructor assigned Mandy to a court with a dark-haired girl whom she had grown to like and two men, one a very tall, stick-thin player and a good-looking, stocky and much shorter man. Mandy realized she'd noticed each of these three players in action, as they'd stood out from the rest. They were clearly the best in the class. She was flattered to be chosen to play with them and only a little intimidated—after all, tennis was her game.

The foursome had the usual trouble getting used to doubles. They'd often find both partners on the same side of the court, at the base line or the net, leaving the court wide open for their opponents to score. Too often each partner would watch politely, each expecting the other to hit the ball, while it flew between them uncontested. Or both would swing for the ball at once, threatening to crack rackets or skulls. Every court resounded with alternating laughter and cursing. But as the workout progressed, they eventually began to smooth out the wrinkles and start to make real headway—just as the period came to an end.

Mandy and Angela, her assigned opponent, sat on the court-side bench to catch their breath and laughed about how rusty they were at doubles. They looked up to see their very tall and thin male counterpart, named Grant, loping back to the gym and their fourth partner walking toward them, smiling, his towel draped around his neck. Mandy squinted as the afternoon sun shone brightly behind him, obscuring his features.

"Nice game, I think," he said, laughing.

"I'm not so sure," replied Angela as she got up to leave. "Sorry, people, but I've gotta run. Gotta fix early dinner and then rush off to three hours of economics tonight. Yucko! See ya tomorrow." She grabbed her things and ran off toward the women's gym. The young man sat down and pretended to straighten the strings on his racket. "We've never actually met," he said, sticking out his hand. "I'm Alan Marsden."

"Hi. Mandy Cartwright." They shook hands.

"That's an interesting name," he said. "Nice."

"Actually it's Amanda, but I don't think anyone but teachers and doctors have ever called me that. You know—names on the lists."

"By the way, I'm glad to see you're feeling better," he said, a bit cryptically.

Surprised, Mandy looked at him blankly. "What do you mean?" she asked.

"Well, a couple of days just before spring break I was in the health center getting a wrist cast removed and I happened to see you leaving with your suitcase and what might've been your parents. I just guessed you'd been there for a couple of days. And I'm glad to see you're better, that's all."

Mandy was only slightly relieved but very curious about him. Who was he, and how much did he know about her?

Alan noticed her discomfort and quickly added, "You're a pretty good player. Been playing long?"

"I taught it during the summer," Mandy said. "You're pretty good yourself." Looking at her watch she saw that it was quarter to five.

"Want to join me for a Coke or something?" Alan asked. "It won't spoil your dinner. I'm thirsty."

Still curious to hear what he knew about her, she smiled and said, "I guess I wouldn't mind a drink or something cold. But I think I'd better hit the showers first."

"Me too. I'll meet you outside the women's gym in twenty minutes, okay?"

Alan Marsden was about five feet, ten inches tall, with a strong face, sandy blonde hair, brown eyes, and a very athletic frame. Mandy had noticed his muscular legs right away—and his powerful serve, much to her chagrin. He was a first-year graduate student in architecture, something of a whiz who had captured the prestigious Herschel B. Reinhold National Scholarship in Architecture, awarded to the nation's outstanding undergraduate scholar in the field. He'd won the award at University of Chicago but had decided to take his master's degree at Farmington, partly because of its superb architecture faculty and the school's proximity to the great Boston-to-Washington "Megalopolis"—without actually being in it—but also because he simply loved backwoods Maine, with its Walden-like pioneer charm, its down-to-earth, straightforward culture, and its easy access to year-round outdoor sports. He loved sports.

After showers they walked downtown in the pleasant afternoon warmth. Alan talked Mandy into having pizza and root beer at Shakey's; after all, they would certainly be getting plenty of exercise to wear off the calories. He was relaxed and talkative. He'd noticed her in the health center and wondered what happened, and hadn't the slightest idea what the problem might have been. He mentioned how lucky she was to have folks that were concerned enough to drive up to see her.

It was clear to them both that they enjoyed each other's company from the start, as they talked lightly over their pitcher of root beer and pepperoni pizza. When Mandy asked Alan how he'd happened to be at Farmington, he made reference to Maine's similarity with Nova Scotia and his early life there. He seemed reluctant to talk about himself; he was anything but self-centered. But Mandy sensed that his was a special story and gently urged him to tell her something about himself.

Alan's parents were dead; when he wasn't in school he lived with an aunt in Glens Falls, upstate New York, at the southern edge of the Adirondacks near Lake George, he explained, but he was originally from Nova Scotia. He'd been on his own since he could remember, since his parents had died. His aunt had taught him early to be independent, not to need anyone, to make his own way in the world. In the course of their conversation Mandy sensed that he was serious but pleasant and down-to-earth. Clearly he worked hard at everything he did; his accomplishments showed that. He asked Mandy questions about herself, but didn't pry. He happened to mention that he thought Mandy was particularly attractive, even after a bout with some sort of problem in the health center, but had been too shy even to say hello until today.

Mandy couldn't help but think of Brent and how smooth and charming he had appeared at first—and the monster he'd turned into. Could Alan be the same way? She had decided not to allow herself to become serious with anyone again, especially physically, after Brent. But Alan appeared to be more a genuinely friendly person, compared to Brent's rather flagrant lady-killer approach to her. Alan seemed truly interested in her, and to Mandy's great relief, his shyness extended apparently to sexual things, and he gave no hint of pushing himself on her. She was still wary, but there was no harm in just talking, was there? The more they talked on that first day and over the weeks that followed, the more relaxed they felt with each other—that was so important to Mandy.

The couple found that their emotional lives complemented each other beautifully. Despite his accomplishments in academics and sports, Alan's life had been tough and sad. His self-confidence certainly required no building up, but his self-esteem was surprisingly low. To him Mandy was bright and fresh, and she lifted his spirits with her spontaneity and general cheerfulness. He found that just being with her somehow lifted him, made him feel really good about himself. And as Mandy spoke about her closeness to her family—especially with her mother—Alan was further drawn to her. He had almost no family of his own. Without his being aware of it, he subconsciously felt that if he could be really close to Mandy, he could appropriate a surrogate family for himself without even having met them.

For her part, Mandy thought he was the kindest, most gentle and understanding person she'd ever met. She needed to be able to trust again. And in spite of the hurt she'd gone through, even though she was still grieving the loss of a part of herself, she honestly believed she could trust this man. He was so mild-mannered, even with his stern, often faraway look. He was gentle and sensitive but so strong, with a burning passion for his work. He had such energy, such accomplishments. Here was a man she could really look up to, whose energy nurtured her, built her own confidence.

She liked the things he liked, and she was amazed at the new world he opened for her. How much he knew about architecture, about sports and natural history! His love for nature fascinated Mandy. On their time off from studies together he took her to nearby Mt. Blue and taught her about trees, ferns and wildflowers, things of nature she'd never even noticed. He took her to the park and demonstrated his prowess with his very expensive recurved bow, later laughingly showing her how easy the fundamentals of archery really are. He took her to the river and showed her how to maneuver a canoe over white water, scaring her half to death. They went to the high school playground where he taught her the finer points of jump-shooting a basketball and how to kick a soccer ball. He was virtually unbeatable at ping pong, horseshoes, lawn darts, and croquet. And he did things with a frisbee that she never dreamed possible. Mandy had never known such a person.

On a Sunday afternoon several weeks into their relationship the couple took their books and a picnic lunch to Clearwater Pond, a few miles northeast of Farmington, where they found a meadow filled with wildflowers overlooking the pond. In the warm sun they spread out a blanket, opened the basket and dug in to fried chicken, a chilled bottle of Napa Valley Riesling, potato salad, pickles, apples, and a big bag of buttered popcorn, for which Alan had a great passion.

During the meal, Mandy mentioned that she wanted to change her major and asked for Alan's opinion to help her decide.

"Why do you want to change?" he asked.

Mandy surprised herself by unhesitatingly telling him the reason. She told him first of her shock at seeing Gordon Farquhar in Longfellow Hall, and then, in tears, she related the story of his molesting her in high school.

Alan immediately became quiet, and Mandy could sense that he was seething inside, but she told him Farquhar had made only one attempt to contact her at Farmington and she had certainly gone out of her way to avoid him. After a few moments Alan took her hands in his.

"I guess it's in the past then, eh?" he said. "What's done is done, and we can't live in the past, can we? But that bastard won't ever touch you again. From here on in, you won't ever have to put up with that kind of crap, I promise."

Mandy mistook his words of anger for those of comfort. In tears for being forgiven, she was so grateful that he loved her and accepted her despite what she'd done. She threw her arms around his neck and, sobbing, repeated "I love you, I love you" over and over.

Alan, a bit uncomfortable with her tears and being grasped around the neck, helped Mandy up, and together they walked down to the water. Taking off their shoes, they rolled up their pantlegs and, holding hands, waded along the sandy shore of the pond. Alan turned and asked, "Well, what do you want to major in?"

"Oh, I don't know," she said. "It just can't be anything related to English or language arts. I don't want to run the risk of ever bumping into him again."

"Why don't you try social science?" he offered. "You can take all sorts of things—psych, sociology, anthropology, geography—and then maybe get a teaching credential for high school or junior high. And you wouldn't need any more English than just the basic ed requirement."

Mandy again threw her arms around his neck again and kissed him. "You're so smart!" she squealed. "I've been struggling with this for months, and you stand there in the water after five seconds and solve my problem. You're an absolute genius!" She hopped up and down in the water as she squeezed his neck.

"Aw shucks, ma'am, 'twarn't really nuthin," he said, twisting his foot and digging his toes into the sand beneath the water.

Mandy laughed at how silly they both looked. It felt so good to laugh again, she thought, and she moved her body close to his. Suddenly the warmth between them changed to desire and Alan pulled her to him, kissing her with such feeling that they almost toppled over. Realizing they were still ankle deep in the water, they retreated, Mandy giggling, to the shore and the comfort of their blanket, the coolness of Riesling and the touch of warm bodies.

It was on a relaxed evening almost two weeks later, while Mandy was visiting Alan in his downtown apartment, that she gathered up her courage and told him about Brent Cutler. She admitted that her visit to the health center before spring break was the result of her terrible experience with the attempted abortion in Boston and that she'd almost died from it. Mandy sat with Alan on the sofa, her head buried against his chest, and with his arms around her, comforting her. Weeping, she poured out her feelings to him as he held her and gently caressed her hair.

Alan, not wishing to hear this, said nothing. He found no words to comfort her, but the silence and his arms around her were enough for Mandy. She felt closer to him than she ever had to anyone. She snuggled closer to him for comfort, wanting his arms to protect her, to keep her safe forever. She didn't dare ask him what his thoughts were, for fear he might scold or reject her. She looked up into his eyes and saw compassion and forgiveness. They became closer, knowing there was truth between them.

For the long Memorial Day weekend at the end of May they decided to take a four-day camping trip to Mt. Katahdin in Baxter State Park, a considerable distance away in the north-central part of the state. Alan promised to show her the place where the sun's rays purportedly first strike the mainland of the United States in the morning—Baxter Peak, the top of the mountain. They would really have to rough it while they were camping, Alan warned, but he was sure Mandy would love it. He was truly excited. Mandy was less enthusiastic, wishing he'd chosen something safer, less risky; but she was thrilled that he'd accepted her and asked her to go with him.

They packed carefully, aware that they'd have to carry everything three miles in to Chimney Pond campground at the base of the mountain. Mandy was surprised that Alan had a complete set of camping gear—sleeping bag, stove, lantern, cooking gear, backpacks, the works. He had borrowed a friend's down bag for Mandy. "By the way," he mentioned, "these two bags just happen to be able to zip together. Sometimes it gets pretty chilly at the base of Katahdin." She just tilted her head and smiled teasingly at him.

He had done most of the food shopping already, picking up dry, high-energy foods that took up minimal space. "We can pick up some dehydrated main courses at L.L. Bean's in Freeport on the way, and some bacon and eggs and a bottle of champagne in Millinocket," he said. "And mosquitoes won't bother us. I even remembered to bring the 6-12."

He let Mandy use his homemade packboard, made from canvas with a lightweight wooden frame, because it was comfortable to carry. "Made it in Explorers years ago," he said smiling and showed her how to pack it. Mandy was simply amazed at how well organized he was, at all the things he could do.

Alan picked up Mandy at five o'clock Friday morning, while it was still dark, so they could reach Millinocket by noon. From there it was twenty-six miles on a winding, unpaved road to the parking area in the state park. Their legs, strong from tennis, had no problem with the steadily uphill three-mile trail through the pines to the campground. Only Mandy's shoulders ached from the straps of the packboard, weighed down with gear. Once she smelled a pungent odor, of what seemed like fermenting berries, damp moss and old tree bark. She turned halfway around on the trail and asked Alan, "What's that smell?"

"Bear. It's okay. Keep going."

She shivered and trudged on, thumbs hooked around the shoulder straps, her eyes nervously scanning the trees. Puffing a bit, she wondered how Alan could be so in harmony with nature, so self-reliant. All of this was so unfamiliar, even frightening at times, yet she found herself comfortable being near him. And she was pleased that she'd been able to win his approval, at least so far. Well, she thought, we'll see what it's like to climb a mountain.

From time to time they saw the rugged grey bulk of the mountain through clearings in the pines as they walked. They rested frequently, but even so, within two hours they came to the last low rise and finally looked down on the campground. Just beyond was the almost circular Chimney Pond and directly behind it, the virtually vertical eastern face of Mt. Katahdin loomed massively above them.

The summer camping season hadn't really begun, and so only a hardy handful of people were yet at the campsite. Among the sparse, tall pines they found a relatively isolated and empty shelter, which was essentially a raised wooden platform for sleeping bags, with a low roof and three log walls. The open front, sheltered by the overhanging roof, contained a bin for dry firewood, and a stone fireplace sat some eight feet beyond the opening. It was perfect, especially for two, especially now.

Their afternoon consisted of unpacking and setting up camp and a brief excursion around the local area to familiarize themselves with the surroundings. After a well-deserved dinner of reconstituted dehydrated hamburger (which turned out a bit like seasoned, tenderized cardboard), macaroni and cheese, fresh spinach and pond-chilled sparkling champagne, they rested contentedly before the fire, sipping from paper cups. Mellowing rapidly, Alan found his chin drooping to his chest; and suddenly realizing his state of near exhaustion after the long drive and arduous trek, he suggested they turn in.

Following trips to their respective washrooms, Alan went for several fat logs to bolster the low fire against the May evening's chill. It would be really cold in the wee hours. But with luck and little wind the logs might last all night. While he was gone Mandy quickly stepped out of her hiking boots, jeans, flannel shirt and underwear and put on sexy, very sheer lace baby dolls she'd bought the week before, dabbed a bit of Shalimar in all the right places, then slipped into the sleeping bags, which she'd zipped together without his knowing. Tonight she would show him just how much she loved and trusted him. She wanted to please him in every way, to give herself completely for his pleasure. The thought of it aroused her as she waited for him in the closing darkness.

Alan returned, dropped the logs into the bin and picked up three of the fattest to build a firepile that would last the night. Feeling groggy, he sat for a moment on the edge of the bin to watch the fire and take off his boots, then stood up and stretched. Turning, he peered into the dimness of the shelter and saw Mandy in the sleeping bag. "Now don't you dare peek," he admonished as he took off his shirt and pants. Climbing hands and knees onto the platform, he failed to notice the sleeping bags were together and pulled aside the corner flap. Startled at seeing Mandy's white breasts outlined through the sheer black lace, he was speechless as she reached up to his chest and began to gently slide her fingers down to his stomach. Leaning upward to kiss his lips, she slid her hand down into his shorts to find his already firm penis pulsing at her touch.

That long night, in the flicker of warm firelight, Mandy demonstrated her love for Alan in a thoroughly convincing way—and he reciprocated in kind. He knew then that this was the woman he wanted to marry.

The couple stayed two more days at Mt. Katahdin, wading in the ice-cold Chimney Pond, climbing the huge boulders at the base of the talus slopes, exploring the countryside in search of white-tailed deer, moose and bears, and attempting one ascent of the mountain. They decided it would be too risky to climb all the way to the top in the dark just to be the first people in the country to see the sun rise. Such a climb would entail their having to traverse a long, almost horizontal section of the mountain called the Knife Edge—in the dark. The slope there fell precipitously on both sides, with only a sharp ridge of boulders separating the two steep inclines. It was indeed a knife edge, dangerous enough in broad daylight. They were content to take the alternative northern route to the top, a much longer hike but infinitely safer.

There, on top of Mt. Katahdin, they sat over a trail lunch of peanuts, raisins, chocolate chips, cheese and crackers, and water. The peak was actually quite flat on the north side, having been sheared off by glaciers thousands of years ago. The slope fell only gradually toward the north and west but dropped as a sheer cliff on the east. With a view overlooking hundreds of miles on all sides, Mandy and Alan knew that from this moment they would start to plan their lives as a couple. Their choices and their dreams henceforth were of togetherness.

From that day her love for him and her confidence in him grew steadily. No longer would Mandy have to search for acceptance; she'd found that and more. She wanted to please him more each day, and so grew more flexible with Alan, bending pliably to his wishes. There was no conflict in their relationship; how could there be? If Alan loved her, nothing could go wrong.

Chapter Ten

The next two years fairly flew by for the lovers. By the end of her junior year Mandy was well into her social science program and had even taken several education courses early to get a jump on the requirements for her teaching credential, as Alan had suggested. He lived in a small apartment off campus, above Green's Drug Store, so Mandy spent less and less time with her friends at the dorm. Being as happy and in love as she was, she honestly didn't miss her friends and the closeness of dorm life. Alan filled her life now. He was everything she could have asked for in a man, and even after more than two years together she could still scarcely believe he could love her in spite of what she had done—because in fact, she could never quite forget what she'd done. In her happiness with Alan, she was unaware that her subconscious guilt had left her self-esteem critically low, that only his love for her kept her feeling alive and happy.

Alan did remarkably well in his master's program, greatly impressing his instructors with his final design project for an enclosed shopping mall, his area of specialization. He was graduating with distinction and surely was headed for a promising career as an architect. Mandy wasn't surprised at all at how well he'd done or that he'd already received job offers from several pretigious architectural firms. She knew his mind was always designing, creating, trying to improve on what was there. He was so confident and terribly ambitious, and Mandy had nothing but admiration for him.

Alan was indeed ambitious. He knew clearly that the world could be his oyster if he played his cards right. He loved Mandy, but his work always came first, because his work was his future. Without being the best, you couldn't have the best. Alan was well aware that Mandy had placed him on a pedestal, that she almost worshiped him. It felt good to have someone care so much. Besides, he certainly cared for her. If only she wouldn't go on about love and togetherness all the time—that made him uncomfortable. And she seemed to cling so much, emotionally as well as physically. He didn't like that. But he didn't like conflicts either, so he never said anything about it. Well, she'd get over that in time, when she got used to things.

Otherwise Mandy was exciting, enthusiastic, a bundle of energy—in several areas—and she was beautiful, poised, a woman certain to enhance his life, his home, his personal prestige and his career possibilities. That was the most important thing—the future. But perhaps just as important, she seemed to lack any real personal ambition except to please him and she made few demands on him for anything. Her goals, if she had any, were unclear in her mind. And that would make it easy to do what he wanted to do; she would conform to his wishes, adjust to *him*. Mandy would want to share in his dreams. Already she'd told him she thought the husband's career came first and that a woman's career came second to her husband's. Her first job was to make a comfortable home for her husband. Yes, she would be perfect.

Alan had proposed to her on a three-day skiing trip to Stowe, Vermont, last Christmas. She'd immediately accepted. He was graduating in June and would be going for a year's post-graduate study at the University of Toronto—and at the same time he'd accepted a part-time position there with Sumner, Boyce and Levine, a leading architectural design firm. If things worked out as he planned, by taking that one more year of study and still being able to work, soon he could go anywhere in the world if he wanted to. Whatever he wanted to. He had a brilliant career ahead as an architect—and he already had a foot in the door of a large, exciting and progressive city.

Mandy's parents were thrilled with the way Mandy's life had come together. They'd seen her so hurt and knew she could be very vulnerable, and now they saw how happy she was and how well suited Alan was for Mandy. Her getting married and having to move to Canada, away from Falmouth and Farmington—where she'd become very much at home—would be a major adjustment, but Mandy's happiness was her parents' foremost consideration. They gave the couple their wholehearted blessing. She could transfer almost all of her academic credits to the University of Toronto and complete her education there, so almost nothing would be lost. And she'd be happy in her new home with her new husband. What could be better for her?

After Alan's graduation in June, he drove back home to Glens Falls to relax and help his aunt with some of the work around the place. About a week later Mandy also took her Volkswagen up to Glens Falls to meet his aunt, and early the next day the couple drove, in his more reliable Chevy, to Toronto to look over the university and the city. To get there was a simple matter. They had only to drive a short distance south, through Saratoga Springs to the thruway at Schenectady, then head west through the Mohawk Valley—on the longest, straightest highway Mandy had ever seen. Six hours later they crossed the border at Buffalo, and within two more hours the skyline of Toronto appeared before them. Mandy was simply astonished at the size of Lake Ontario, at the edge of which Toronto spread out. Could this huge thing be a lake? It looked more like the ocean, but without the waves.

As they drove along the lakeshore and neared the city, Mandy saw the skyline close up for the first time and had a strange feeling she'd seen it before. She often had glimpses of déja vu but would brush them aside as the wanderings of an overactive imagination. She remembered her parents telling her she had too much imagination. But the feeling persisted.

Mandy's first impression of the city was that it was so beautiful—and clean! This was nothing like Boston, even though the two cities were about the same size. There was no litter lining the gutters or blowing around the streets, no dank odors rising from sewers and manholes, no cramped, dilapidated and dirty brick tenements, no garbage piled on street corners. And the streets didn't wind and curve willy-nilly in and out of each other as they did in Boston. They were largely straight and at right angles to each other in a sort of gridiron pattern. She suddenly realized it would be difficult to get lost in Toronto and immediately began to like the city. Everything was so big and modern and spread out in such an organized pattern. She felt excited about the prospect of living here.

They checked in at the Lakeshore Motel at the western edge of the city and spent the next day and a half exploring Toronto and the university. Alan took Mandy over to the architecture department so they could meet some of the faculty there; and they welcomed him with clear satisfaction. The department head went out of his way to introduce Alan and Mandy to the few faculty who were available, then he showed the couple through the building, spending much time in the studios emphasizing the facilities. At first Mandy was excited, but she soon became bored with the studios. They all looked alike to her, all vaguely bizarre with the strange structures, some life-size and some in miniature. Alan became caught up in some sort of magic that he felt there, but Mandy just became more and more uncomfortable.

The couple then drove over to Bay Street so Alan could introduce himself to the people at Sumner, Boyce and Levine, where he'd be working in the fall. There, too, the staff fell over backwards to welcome Alan into their fold, even if it would only be part time— at first. Quite obviously Charles Sumner wanted to make it clear that Alan was free to stay indefinitely, and on a full-time basis.

"My boy," he said paternally, "This is the city of the future. There aren't quite two million people here now, but our projections indicate double that figure in little more than twenty years. The sky's the limit for you. This could be your home, your family. Think about it, son."

"Thank you, sir," Alan replied. Then he carefully added, "I'm sure there will be an opportunity for us both to assess the future. Perhaps then we can talk about possibilities. I have to think about what's best for my wife and family."

He smiled and stuck out his hand, which Sumner took and held. "We're looking forward to having you aboard, son. Good luck in your move. If there's anything we can do to help, you let us know."

Alan noted that Sumner's offer, apparently generous and kind, lacked specificity; he was offering nothing without Alan's having to ask for it.

"Thank you, sir," he repeated. He and Mandy both smiled, then turned and went out to the elevator. She somehow expected the people at the architecture department and at Sumner, Boyce and Levine to be at least cordial in their welcome, but she was amazed at the way they treated Alan like a sort of minor deity. As the couple left the building Alan felt good, even marvelous, at the way things had gone, and so did Mandy. She squeezed his arm in hers and held on in wonder and great admiration for her man.

For Mandy this was to be a busy summer in Falmouth. She found herself quite busy preparing for their August wedding, a simple family affair with about fifty guests altogether. But the details took an enormous amount of thought and time. Then there were the piles of forms and applications that she had to fill out for immigration to Canada and for the University of Toronto. Alan, having been born in Nova Scotia, had maintained his Canadian citizenship and had no problem either going to school or working in Canada, but Mandy was an "alien" on both counts. As an American and therefore an alien as far as Canada was concerned, she would have to apply for status as a "landed immigrant." Every time she saw the word "alien" on the forms, she chuckled. What a terrible word; it made her feel like a creature from outer space. I didn't see any difference in those people, she thought. Then out loud she added, "Eh?"

During all this time Mandy saw little of Alan. He'd gone off to Toronto to find an apartment and become acquainted with the buildings and the few enclosed shopping malls in and around Toronto. And he wanted to learn more about both the architecture department at the university—particularly the politics—and the firm of Sumner, Boyce and Levine. Several times a week he would call Falmouth or she would call the motel in Toronto, mostly to make sure of decisions surrounding the wedding or to give news about the household items they'd received as shower gifts. It was a surreal time for Mandy. All the attention. With her parents and Alan largely in control of the wedding arrangements, Mandy seemed to be on remote control as she flitted from one activity to another, almost numb with excitement, carrying out the details. She had no time to think about what might lie ahead.

Standing in her gorgeous gown as if in a daze, Mandy stared back at her reflection in the mirror. This was her day. Her wedding day. In minutes she would become Mrs. Alan Marsden. She liked the sound of it. Mandy Marsden. She had found her prince, just like in the fairy tales, and they would live happily ever after. Her nesting instinct was becoming strong; she was so ready to be a wife, she thought. If she had been even a little introspective, however, she would have seen that beneath all the white lace and taffeta and flowers was still a confused little girl, one who was really frightened at what was happening to her—and what had happened to her. But such thoughts never occurred to her in the face of her current bliss. She was in seventh heaven. It was her day, the special one she'd prepared for. And her man was waiting for her at the altar.

Ralph and Anne spared no expense in giving Mandy and Alan a beautiful wedding send-off, complete with a rented limousine and a champagne dinner reception at Tecumseh Country Club, with entertainment from a small string ensemble, later followed by a musical group more appropriate for dancing. "After all," Ralph said proudly, "we've only got one daughter to spoil." Secretly, however, he regretted having spent so much, but then again, everyone would be reading about this bash in the paper, so one had to be careful to make a good appearance for the townsfolk.

The newly married couple spent a wonderful week on a honeymoon cruise in the Bahamas. They stayed at an island resort right out of "Tales of the South Pacific," they thought—though Alan noted it was the wrong ocean—but for a week the newlyweds were lost in each other. "So this is heaven," Mandy said to herself. "It's wonderful. I hope it never ends. I'm going to be the best wife in the world."

Too soon Mandy and Alan had to return to Massachusetts and almost immediately leave for Toronto. School and work awaited Alan, and there wasn't much time to spare. Mandy gave Brad her hand-me-down Volkswagen as a going-away present, warning him to be easy on her old friend so it would last at least a year longer.

Then came a teary goodbye as the couple finished loading Mandy's belongings and a few pieces of furniture into the rented trailer that would follow Alan's Chevy into Canada. Then, after what seemed only a whirlwind stop in Falmouth, they were on the road and headed for a new life in a new country, leaving Ralph, Anne and Brad waving on the sidewalk as they watched the trailer move out of sight.

The emigrants, as they called themselves, drove carefully through Massachusetts, trying to memorize the beauty of the Berkshire Hills, and into New York and up to Glens Falls. There Alan loaded the remainder of his belongings, which he had packed and set aside on his earlier trip; and after their quick lunch with his aunt, they kissed her goodbye and again headed out onto the long highway westward.

It was dinner time when the car and trailer, with the two tired travelers, pulled up to the border station just across the Niagara River. Only then did Mandy realize that there were two towns called Niagara Falls, one in Canada and one in the United States. At the customs station on the edge of the bridge she saw in the distance that the Canadian Niagara Falls was clearly the one with the attractions. Certainly the falls themselves—Horseshoe Falls—were most spectacular on the Canadian side. American Falls, on the American side, was far less impressive. Well, they would get plenty of opportunity to view the falls; but for now, they had to clear customs.

On their earlier trip to Toronto the passage across the border was a simple matter. The Canadian official in the booth simply had asked if they were carrying gifts or liquor or firearms and waved them through without so much as a second blink. On this occasion, however, there seemed to be a problem. The uniformed woman in the booth seemed very abrupt and impersonal in her questioning. Alan told her their immediate plan—to move to Toronto for school and part-time work—and tried to hand her the papers, all of which seemed to be in good order. But she would have none of it, demanding that they pull the car and trailer into a parking slot nearby.

Mandy became frightened and grasped Alan's arm. "What's wrong? What are they doing? Why are they doing this?"

"I don't know, but we have to do what they want."

He pulled the car over, and two customs officials walked over and asked to see the papers, which included a general list of all their belongings in the trailer.

"Let's go inside," one said.

They escorted the couple into the customs building and proceeded to examine the papers in great detail, it seemed to Mandy. Shaking, she took a seat on a nearby bench while Alan waited at the counter for the men to finish. She couldn't hear the sporadic conversation between Alan and the officials, and was glad of it. She wanted only to be allowed to enter the country in peace.

As Mandy sat nervously fidgeting on the bench, a paunchy, grey-haired customs official appeared at the counter and called out,

"Mrs. Amanda Marsden?"

Startled, she stood up and identified herself, and the man said, "Come with me, please."

Mandy glanced apprehensively at Alan as she walked over to the official. The man said he had to ask her a few questions and showed her the entrance to a small office. Alan nodded his assurance and she went inside. The official closed the door.

The room seemed cold and stark, and Mandy's fear began to intensify, though she didn't know why. She hadn't done anything wrong. She glanced at a formal portrait of the queen on the wall and then noticed a single lamp suspended from the center of the ceiling and with two chairs immediately below.

"Have a seat, miss," the man gestured as he went behind his desk. Then the questions began. "How much money are you bringing to Canada? Do you plan to send for any more?"

Mandy did her best to answer according to her understanding of their finances.

"Are you aware that your husband must sponsor you in Canada for a period of five years? That means if you break a law or do not live with him, you could be deported. Do you understand what I'm saying, miss?"

She understood. He was telling her to toe the line with both her husband and the law.

"Do you understand that as an alien landed immigrant, you will have no voting rights or privileges?" She understood. She would be a second-class citizen as well. It felt as if she were on trial, a fugitive brought in for the third degree.

Finally his questions ended and, apparently pleased with Mandy's answers, he rose from his chair and gestured for her to leave. Greatly relieved to be finished and to see Alan, she went back to the bench and waited.

After some time the two men dealing with the paperwork came back around the counter and Alan followed them outside, a scowl of frustration on his face. Mandy went after them, thinking they could now leave. The men walked to the car and asked Alan to open the doors and trunk, which he did. One of them reached into the back seat and began pawing through their belongings, apparently

92

searching for something, while the other did the same in the trunk. Evidently satisfied—or at least not having found what they were after—they then walked to the back of the trailer and told Alan to open the door.

"Okay, let's start unloading," one of them said to Alan.

"You've got to be kidding!" he protested. Mandy watched in horror as a great argument ensued between Alan and the customs officials. She broke down in tears as she watched Alan, terribly angry, remove their boxes, clothes and furniture from the trailer and the customs men open and examine everything. After an hour most of their things were on the ground, opened and gone through. Helpless and frustrated, Mandy cried through the whole ordeal.

Finally the customs men stood up and one handed the papers to Alan. "All right," he said. "You can repack and go on through. Sorry for this, but we have to be careful."

"Is that all you're going to do?' demanded Alan, outraged. "Is that it?"

"You can go through now," the man repeated, and he turned with the other official and went inside, leaving their goods scattered on the ground.

Alan, standing limply, simply looked over at Mandy and shook his head. "I don't believe this." She walked over to him and put her arms around his waist. She began to cry again.

"Shit!" he exclaimed ferociously, ignoring Mandy's hurt. "Well, hell, give me a hand and we'll get this stuff back in and then get the hell out of here."

In silence they reloaded the trailer, unconcerned with the arrangement of packing, Mandy traumatized by insecurity and the strangeness of the situation, Alan enraged with bureaucracy, both fatigued and uncaring for the other's distress.

It was ten-thirty in the evening when they officially, finally, crossed into Canada at Niagara Falls. Still furious, Alan drove faster than caution might have suggested as they looked for their motel. Later, exhausted and angry and after three quick beers, Alan tumbled into bed not caring whether Mandy did or not.

For the first time, the couple had encountered conflict that affected them both differently, and neither had responded to the other's need. It was an inauspicious beginning for their lives together in Canada.

The newly arrived couple spent the next morning in Niagara Falls visiting a "wild animal" farm and a wax museum, hanging over the rail for a misty look at Horseshoe Falls. After a quick lunch at a rather unclean restaurant near the falls they climbed into the car and, trailer behind them, made their way out to the highway leading to Toronto. As if the border incident never happened, neither mentioned it. In little more than two hours they pulled up to their new apartment downtown in their new city.

"Well, Mrs. Marsden, here we are," said Alan.

Chapter Eleven

Life in Toronto began well for the newlywed couple despite their fearful experience at the border. Alan had found a pleasant and spacious sixth-floor, two-bedroom apartment in what was considered uptown Toronto, some blocks north of the university; the largest stores and office buildings, including that of Sumner, Boyce and Levine, were apparently "downtown," though Mandy never quite understood the distinction. Their apartment was rather expensive, but money wasn't a problem for them. Alan's part-time work at Sumner, Boyce and Levine paid the rent and left enough for groceries. Other expenses were met by the university; even before they'd arrived Alan was listed in the fall course schedule as teacher of a section of Introduction to Architecture. As a teaching assistant, that meant his tuition was lowered to only a token payment, and he received $350 a month in addition, just for teaching one course.

The couple was delighted that their income even allowed them to haunt second-hand furniture shops, where they picked up a double bed and dresser, a pair of floor lamps, a comfortable if somewhat worn sofa and a dinette set to add to the things Mandy's parents had contributed. A few colorful posters on the walls and innumerable little potted plants, placed everywhere, completed the decor.

Superficially, life in downtown Toronto was very similar to what might be found in Boston. Mandy's few experiences there more or less prepared her for the initial shock of living in the big city; nevertheless, the first few months of married life were very difficult for her. Toronto was nothing like slow-moving, sheltered Falmouth or even the more energetic Farmington, with its bustling university population of 9,000. And dozens of unexpected small differences posed small problems for Mandy and confused her, so many things to adapt to. Naturally, she turned to Alan whenever some new difficulty confronted her.

Alan, however, had quickly become comfortable in his new surroundings, having been used to the hustle and bustle of Chicago and having already spent part of the summer in Toronto. Soon after the couple moved in, he'd become caught up in his work at the firm and at school. Often preoccupied with his many new responsibilities, he drove himself with characteristic fervor, believing himself to be in competition with his fellow graduate students and peers at work. To meet his self-imposed expectations required that virtually every moment be dedicated to reaching perfection on the job and learning more than his professors knew. These, he understood, were the keys to success.

Consequently, Alan neither understood nor cared to understand Mandy's sudden insecurities and her frequent need to grasp at him both physically and emotionally. He would peel her arms from his neck while trying to back away. "There's no problem with this," he'd say. "Think about it and work it out yourself."

Mandy noticed that Alan approached situations rationally. He'd use his head to figure out the problem, determine its cause and establish the most appropriate solution, given the salient variables. As a result, he had few problems; that is, those that he recognized as problems. In contrast, Mandy came at life more reactively, and she tended to rely more on her feelings in her responses. Consequently she constantly doubted herself, wondering why she was so stupid not to be able to see things as he did.

Often he would arrive home in time for dinner with every intention of returning to the college library afterward. Mandy's doleful "Do you have to go out again?" would provoke terse, impatient answers. "Yes. I've got work to do. How else do you expect me ever to do well?" And the door would close on her, leaving her alone in the silent apartment to solve her problems herself.

Mandy also attended the university, having enrolled in three courses, but she only went through the motions. She somehow couldn't find enthusiasm for her studies. Alan encouraged her to become more independent, perhaps even get a part-time job—anything to occupy her mind and time. She wasn't interested; she wanted her husband and his understanding. When he kept pulling away, she started to feel as if she were alone, and slowly, over the weeks, an almost subconscious fear built within her, a fear of being alone in a strange city and unable to cope emotionally. She began to resent Alan's coolness and self-assuredness. He had his goals and dreams and even his own new friends at work and school, whom she scarcely knew. He was both very popular with them and very busy, but he seemed to have very little time for his wife.

He thrived on his success, and it almost made Mandy jealous. She was playing the role of the good wife, as she should; she was doing what was expected of her, with no idea of what she personally wanted out of life. She was bored, restless, and virtually alone in the crowded city.

Whenever she pictured Alan having coffee with his friends at school, she'd recognize that the only people she knew at all were people in his world. Why hadn't she made new friends of her own? What was the matter with her? She felt very homesick at times and missed her friends at Farmington and Falmouth. But by now they wouldn't be there either; they'd be scattered all over the place just as she was. She felt scattered, as if pieces of her lay in various parts of the northeast. She felt anything but whole.

The couple found themselves bickering about small things. Mandy, jealous of the time Alan spent with his friends at work, complained about it. She frequently made phone calls to Falmouth to talk with her mother, and Alan didn't appreciate either the phone bills or her apparently constant need to rely on her parents. Wasn't she an adult? Couldn't she face these small difficulties straight on and overcome them? What's the big problem anyway? And why does she have to share their intimate lives with her mother all the time? Isn't that a bit immature? Certainly they could handle things themselves. Slowly came the realization that the honeymoon was over.

Partly to give Mandy something to occupy her mind, but mainly to get her off his back, Alan strongly urged that she take a part-time job on campus, in a health food store. They needed someone right away. Maybe this could help relieve her boredom. But Mandy wasn't particularly bored; her husband just didn't understand her needs. Nevertheless, she dutifully agreed to apply for the job, without thinking about whether or not she really wanted it. Besides, she thought this might help her pull up her socks and become a stronger, more independent person. She was surprised to learn that she got the job.

Mandy really loved Alan and the last thing she wanted was to be a burden for him, especially since school and work consumed so much of his time and energy. She resolved to shield from him how insecure and confused she was over the details of life in this new environment. The prospect of having to travel on the subway, for example, terrified her at first, primarily because of the horror stories she'd heard about traveling on the Boston and New York subways. She did her best never to go near it. Then late one morning Alan called and invited her to lunch. Some of the people at Sumner, Boyce and Levine were having their wives meet them at Cicero's downtown, and maybe Mandy would enjoy coming along. Mandy was delighted until she remembered Alan had the car; she'd have to take the subway—alone!

Scared half to death Mandy stood, legs wobbly, at the entrance to the stairway that led down below the sidewalk and into the dark cavern of the subway tunnel. Well, here goes nothing, she thought, and with a deep breath she headed downward. She was startled at the bright lights and shining tiles on the walls, the clean floors and how well-dressed and normal everyone appeared. This was nothing like the Boston subway! There were no spray-painted smears, no graffiti anywhere, no drunks passed out on the floor, no gangs roaming the tunnels. Everything was just the same as on the street above; it was simply underground. Then she realized her fears were entirely unfounded. That old morale booster from Franklin Roosevelt crossed her mind: "...nothing to fear except fear itself." Mandy added, "Yes, and the bogey man." Vastly relieved, she became angry with herself and vaguely wondered why everything seemed to frighten her so. No answer came.

Mandy had mixed feelings about shopping in Toronto. It seemed to take much more time than in the States. (She'd learned that Canadians never say "United States," as all Americans do, but instead commonly say "the U.S." or "the States," which she concluded was more economical.) For one thing, many of the brand names were different and things seemed to be packaged or sized differently. She had trouble finding things on the shelves and then making choices when she did find them.

Shopping therefore took twice as long as in "the States." But she loved to try to read the French side of the labels, which listed the ingredients and perhaps a word of caution about using the product. Largely in frustration with his wife, Alan left the household duties, including shopping, to her. He couldn't understand why she seemed to dawdle so much in the stores, how she could get so hung up in deciding what cut of meat to buy. Once, by herself, she went looking for a nice steak for their dinner, a western cut. She pored over the packages at length but failed to find the western cuts. In desperation she finally knocked on the window behind which the butchers were cutting and packaging their meats, whereupon one of them came out and asked her what she wanted. Laughing, he walked to the display rack and lifted out a package of New York steaks. "This is a western cut," he said. Embarrassed and without even looking over the selection, she took the package from the butcher, placed it in her cart and stalked off.

On another occasion she bought a package of what were labeled "fast-fry" pork chops. Mandy thought that was only a suggestion for cooking, not a direction. That night she left the kitchen in tears when a candlelight dinner she was preparing went up in smoke because she had baked the three little chops for an hour. She hated herself and wouldn't believe Alan when he said it didn't matter. It did matter; she was a failure.

Arguments seemed to occur more frequently. They were fueled primarily by Mandy's constant underlying insecurities and her need to rely on Alan, as well as his dislike of being grasped at and leaned upon. Alan was altogether too rational for Mandy to win an argument, so she would either run weeping to the bedroom after arguments or say nothing, to avoid the argument. In that case, however, the silence and lack of resolution simply built up anxiety in her.

A further aggravation centered on the housework. Mandy was very fastidious in her cleaning and took pride in keeping everything spotless. To her this was her major job and she became frustrated and angry when Alan didn't even notice or seem to care. Because of her habit of keeping a constantly clean house, he quite naturally began to take it for granted. On the other hand, when he came home from a particularly grueling day during which Mandy had spent much of the day at school and her job at the health food store, he found things scattered around the apartment and dirty dishes in the sink. There simply hadn't been time to clean up beforehand; but Alan flew off the handle: "What have you done all day?"

Mandy generally tried to please her husband in as many ways as she could. She'd try to coax him into bed as often as possible. She craved being held, and sex was a major part of their happy times, till Alan noticed that she seemed to demand more and more of his time, which he resented. In fact, resentment was eating at them both, but they didn't know it and certainly never expressed those particular feelings.

Then something happened that completely changed the worsening situation. It came as a distinct surprise because Mandy had been taking birth control pills, but they were both excited and happy about the prospect of becoming a complete family. It was late June, and they'd been married less than a year. Mandy was thrilled to be pregnant, almost bursting to call her parents and tell them the news. She knew this time it was right and she was so thankful to be given another chance. She felt forgiven in God's eyes. It was meant to be. There was no need now to devise a grand dream or choose some noble goal for her life. She could be a mother; that would make her complete. Having a baby was a woman's greatest role, she thought, and she wanted so much to be a mother. She didn't care if it was a girl or boy, just healthy. Please, God.

Because their apartment building was restricted to adults only, they had to move. Neither minded terribly; Alan's school year was finished and he'd started working full time with Sumner, Boyce and Levine, the firm's having made an attractive offer for him to stay on. Their financial situation had also taken a giant step in the right direction, and they could now afford a newer, larger place and new furniture. After some ten days of searching, they located a perfect townhouse in the suburb of Willowdale, a few miles to the north. It was adjacent to a meandering, linear park that boasted a gentle ravine with a quiet stream flowing through it. Squirrels, a rabbit or two, and even a raccoon family gave it something of a country appeal.

Mandy loved the new townhouse and the setting. She took great interest in decorating it, which greatly relieved Alan. His work load was increasing, which required more time on his part, and Mandy seemed happier and more content now that she was pregnant. School could wait now; it would always be there later. She dove headlong into preparations for her new role, reading everything she could find about having a healthy baby, planning the nursery and decorating it in orange and white. That would be bright and cheerful for either a boy or girl. What a good mother and wife she would be. Alan was immensely grateful to see her finally settle down with a purpose, to see her moods take an upward turn and stay there. And he felt good that she was content to stay home except for her shopping trips and her childbirth classes; that too was fine for him.

At one of the classes Mandy learned of a new method of delivery that involved self-hypnosis of the mother. Apparently babies could be delivered more safely and naturally if mother placed herself into a sort of euphoric trance that would relax the body and reduce anxiety. Skeptical, Alan thought little of the notion but agreed to accompany Mandy to the next class, where the procedure was explained more thoroughly. The young doctor seemed competent and showed Alan just how easily Mandy could enter into a relaxed state, reassuring him all the while that nothing could possibly go wrong. To demonstrate his point, while Mandy sat in a trance he slowly pushed a long, thin needle completely through her hand as a stunned Alan stared, unable to speak. There was no blood, and later Mandy simply laughed off his concern for her safety.

Together they attended the classes, and Alan reluctantly agreed to go along with the self-hypnosis technique for Mandy. As time went on, however, Alan frankly grew bored with the classes and stopped attending. Mandy became moody again, becoming demanding and aggravated by little things. By the eighth month their sexual activity had decreased to the point that, except for the odd kiss, there was no touching between them. Both became preoccupied with their respective interests—Alan his work and Mandy her baby.

As the days of the term grew to a close Mandy lost all sensual desire and had become a bit afraid of the delivery. The target date came and went, and for a week, feeling big as a house, she waited restlessly, her anxiety and blood pressure steadily increasing. Finally, late one evening, her water broke and they went to the hospital—just a few minutes' drive—hand in hand and in silence.

In the labor room Alan sat beside Mandy, holding her hand in his as she lay in bed and tried to concentrate on relaxing. Eventually she placed herself in a state of hypnosis, telling herself to stay relaxed, that everything would be all right, that her body should respond to the doctor's orders.

Despite regular attendance by a nurse, who efficiently checked his wife's condition and noted the relevant information on the chart, Alan became slightly disturbed. Even though the doctor hadn't yet arrived, Mandy seemed to be making no progress as the hours slowly passed. Was something wrong?

Doctor Benjamin finally entered the room to sit with Mandy for a few minutes. After asking her a few questions, he left.

Shortly afterward the nurse entered again, and as was her custom she asked how Mandy felt. Each time Mandy would reply that she was fine, she was comfortable and relaxed. Nothing was wrong; everything was going well.

In fact, her body was so numbed by the hypnotic trance that nothing was going well. Her cervix wasn't dilating properly and the muscles weren't reacting; she was too relaxed. And she was becoming dehydrated. Instead of realizing she was terribly thirsty and that something was indeed wrong, she would state mechanically that she was fine, comfortable and relaxed, everything was going well. Her responses were anything but normal; she had convinced herself of a lie.

As a result, the dangerously prolonged labor became extremely difficult to monitor because of Mandy's altered state. To make matters worse, her doctor wasn't available again until the early evening. Alan sat perplexed and anxious with his wife, and after some sixteen hours of waiting for something to happen, he became fed up and stomped out to the nurses' station, demanding that someone do something. He had seen more babies born than any other father in the waiting room.

Even with Doctor Benjamin's arrival the situation hadn't improved. Still the hours passed.

Finally, after more than an incredible twenty-nine hours at the hospital, Doctor Benjamin entered to reassure Alan that soon the ordeal would be over, that two other doctors had been called in for consultation. Would he please leave the room? The door closing, the doctor sat close to Mandy's bed, leaned over and almost whispered, "Mandy, can you hear me?"

"Yes... Can't you get this over with?"

"Yes, right away, but I need a few answers for my report."

He proceeded to ask Mandy questions, to which she responded mechanically, dully: "What are you feeling right now? Can you feel the baby pushing down? Can you tell me the sex? Do you think it's a boy or a girl?" Even through the sedatives and her trance, anger—no, insight—suddenly flashed in Mandy's mind at the last questions. This man wasn't interested in her at all. He was using her, doing some kind of experiment! Angrily, absolutely certain of the baby's sex—she could feel it clearly—she lied: "It's a boy."

The doctors finally decided to take the baby through caesarean section because the baby's life was now in danger. Mandy was so tired and weak by now, she didn't care how the baby was to come as long as it happened soon. Within minutes of the decision she was put to sleep and a beautiful baby girl, Stephanie, was born. Alan saw her first as they wheeled her by the waiting room in an incubator, all covered in blood and birth fluid and with the umbilical cord still freshly cut. He was reassured by the nurse that his daughter would be looking much better in a few moments after they cleaned her up.

Mandy didn't see her baby till the next day. She was so drugged and sleepy that she wasn't sure if she was dreaming when they put a warm, pink bundle beside her on the bed. Tears filled her eyes when she saw how beautiful Stephanie was. She was so grateful that she couldn't help but breathe a silent prayer of thanks to God for this wonderful feeling of joy. She was bursting with happiness, particularly since she could share her joy with Alan and her parents, who had flown up for a few days to help out. Alan could hardly have kept the new grandparents away.

Over the next two days Mandy was too caught up in the hospital routine and learning how to breast feed Stephanie to notice that her body was becoming feverish and she was growing weaker.

Once she tried to sit up to prepare for her baby's being brought into the room, when she felt a sharp pain in her lower abdomen that sent waves of shudders through her body. Frightened, her first impulse was to stand, thinking to get help, when the whole room began to spin. She felt a numbness as she collapsed across the bed just as a nurse entered carrying the little one.

For the next twelve hours Mandy lapsed in and out of consciousness, occasionally mumbling gibberish. The staff psychiatrist recommended she be placed in the psychiatric ward for observation. But by midnight she'd gone into a twilight sleep that baffled everyone.

Alan and her parents couldn't believe it. How could this be happening? Mandy was in a coma! She wasn't even expected to live because her body was so riddled with infection. It was only later that they learned her kidneys had failed, that she had a rare disorder called decimating intravascular coagulation, which was unpredicted because her body showed no signs of symptoms until she fell into the coma. Worse, every free germ in the hospital seemed to have entered her vulnerable body. She was wracked with illness, even in the coma.

Alan and Anne spent the next days pushing for as much attention to Mandy's state as possible, to find a solution to her critical condition. Anne stayed by her bed for much of the time, insisting that she remain despite objections of the hospital staff. Even as they worked, Anne looked on from a corner of the room.

Above the small crowd milling about the bed, Mandy drifted as if in a cloud. There seemed to be confusion. She heard people crying, talking about her death, about what to do with Stephanie. Someone suggested to Alan that he give thought to how he might manage, alone, with a new baby. Familiar voices faded in and out. Everyone kept crying. Mandy looked up and out past her window, and a figure, a huge face, surrounded by what appeared to be a beautiful garden, filled the whole window. The face beckoned to her somehow. Then she was whirling, spiraling down a dark tunnel. The face returned, expressionless and silent, hovering in front of her. She pleaded, begged the face for her life, to be able to be a good wife and mother. She wanted more than anything to stay in the world. Darkness swirled and fell on her.

Then she seemed to hear herself screaming. Oh, how she

wanted to close her eyes, but couldn't. A booming voice kept saying, "If you do, you'll be gone." There was a sharp pain, as if her head were exploding inside, then silence. A quietness enveloped her.

From far away, it seemed, Mandy heard men's voices calling her name, then nearer. Slowly she opened her eyes, hearing again, "Mandy, do you know what day it is?" "How old are you?" "Mandy, do you know where you are?" As her mind cleared and her vision began to focus, she saw the faces and recognized one of the doctors. Hospital, baby—now she remembered it. She knew where she was and she knew why. But not much else. It was so hard to concentrate. What day was it? I'm not sure how old I am, is it 22 or 23? A nurse entered her view, smiling warmly. There were a few anxious people waiting for her to wake up, she said, and she would call them now.

There was a room full of hugs and kisses when Alan and Mandy's parents entered the room. Anne tried to explain to Mandy what had happened to her without going into detail, thinking to gloss over the seriousness of the problem and thus protect her from concern. She'd been in a coma for a few days due to a serious infection. She was going to be all right, but because her kidneys had failed, the doctors would have to drain the toxins from her system. But there was nothing to worry about now; everything would be all right. Mandy tried to listen patiently, not really comprehending the seriousness of the matter, until she couldn't bear it any more. "Where's my baby?" she cried out.

"Oh, she's fine, honey, growing like a weed," said Anne. "You'll be able to see her soon. But first you have to rest and do exactly what the doctors say. I'm going to stay on to look after things with Alan, but Dad has to go back to Falmouth tomorrow, now that we know you're out of the woods. You gave us all a real scare."

Mandy was terribly sorry she'd caused so much worry for everyone, that she had burdened Alan with a new baby to care for by himself, that she'd caused her parents to have to spend a lot of money in coming to Toronto. But what could she do? What could she have done to prevent it? She felt terrible guilt; she'd failed her family again. Even the doctors and nurses should be caring for really sick people, not her. So she tried her best to comply with their requests and orders, to submit willingly to all the blood tests and scans and x-rays. It was the least she could do.

She began to realize just how sick she was when a nurse asked her if she wanted to sit up in bed for the first time. Her bandaged abdomen was uncomfortable, and for some reason her chest was also bound up in bandages. This she accepted stoically; there must be some reason. Then she saw her knees. They were terribly swollen, like two basketballs. And they seemed full of fluid. She was horrified. As she brought her hands to her cheeks, she realized her face was swollen as well. How horrible I must look, she thought. Curiously, everyone who came to her bedside was kind to her; no one seemed to look at her any differently. She was very conscious to notice if she repulsed anyone. Alan, who came with Anne to visit every day, was wonderfully gentle, though he was uncharacteristically quiet during his visits. Anne and he spent most of their visits talking about what Stephanie was doing at home. Mandy couldn't wait to be home with her new baby and her husband.

Three weeks passed, and by then most of the swelling had disappeared and Mandy was growing stronger every day. No further signs of trouble had developed. Now all that had to be done was a final brain scan, besides regular kidney tests. Since her body had been in such shock, the doctors were making sure that all was well.

Mandy was becoming impatient and mildly irritable, even beginning to complain about the same bland food every day. Clearly, she was improving. The nurses began to tease her about being waited on literally hand and foot, but that when she got home she'd have to do the same for her baby. Mandy was growing impatient to leave, to be home, to be with her child finally. She felt wonderful about the prospect. But something was gnawing at the back of her mind. Some vague darkness rested there, some hint that not all was right. She tried to identify what was eating at her, but her mind wasn't clear enough to figure it out, and she became fatigued. Her mind simply wasn't functioning right. Maybe that was it—everyone was so interested in patching up her body that no one seemed concerned about her mind, her feelings. Every physical effect had been assessed, measured, diagnosed and corrected, but no one had ever asked her how she really felt, in her mind, emotionally. Exhausted from trying to think, she looked up at the lights on the white ceiling and watched them become a blur as she dropped off to sleep for the last time in the ward.

Before going home the next day Mandy had to say goodbye to all the doctors and nurses who'd treated her. She had presents or cards for everyone who'd helped her so much. She was grateful for their treatment of her and still felt like a great burden to everyone for getting sick, for being in the hospital for more than a month. It was a big step to be going home to her new job as mother.

Holding little Stephanie for only the second time, Mandy couldn't stop the tears of joy. She sat and rocked the little bundle gently, gazing at every beautiful part. Her eyes were so bright and blue, her hair so fair and curly. That cute little button nose, and those tiny fingers. It was all too wonderful. Mandy just lay her head back against the chair and prayed, thanking God for this gift. She was absolutely going to be the best mother.

But she grew tired easily and found herself flopping into a chair every hour or so for a few days. And she was impatient with herself when she still had to rest so much. She was grateful that her mother had stayed to help out, but she too eventually had to get back to Falmouth. Thank goodness Stephanie was a good baby.

With time, Mandy's illness faded and the Marsdens fell into the typical young family routine, centering mainly around Stephanie's wants or needs. Alan, delighted with a daughter to brag about at work, resumed his increasingly successful career. He was also pleased that Mandy was well and could resume her wifely role. Neither one thought it necessary to talk of the past.

It was easy for Mandy to become caught up in the business of keeping the house and her family. There was always something to do, and she was happy to do it. Alan, too, always was busy with his work, always seemed preoccupied with his calendar of events and preparing for them. And as the months progressed, the times increased when he had to travel to other cities for conferences and consultations. Time seemed to fly by, unnoticed by either of them with their busy schedules.

Before they both realized, little Stephanie would be having her second birthday.

Their lives together developed a pattern that was fairly

common for young married couples starting a family. They had come to measure their happiness by the material possessions they collected and the number of activities—mostly entertaining friends—they could squeeze into their weekends. There was little intimate time between them, except for their delightful episodes playing with Stephanie on the floor; and there was never any discussion about Mandy's previous problems, but neither seemed to notice.

Mandy became almost a compulsive, perfectionist housewife, thinking this would please Alan. Besides, she believed that because he was so successful in his work, she should be just as successful in hers. It amounted to a silent, unannounced competition.

To Mandy, something else seemed still lacking in their marriage. She sensed that Alan probably should be giving her more attention and reassurance, and didn't think that to be any more demanding than needing to eat or sleep. But it also seemed somehow rather silly to confront him with these insignificant little needs, so she kept quiet. After all, he did need to concentrate on his work. In turn, Alan also wanted her care and consideration, even the occasional pipe-and-slippers-by-the-fire treatment. But their timing was terrible. She was either attending to Stephanie or some other household work that had to be done—and therefore wasn't available at his unspoken whim—or he was involved with meeting some project deadline or other work preparations and wasn't aware of her unvoiced needs. Communication and sexual intimacy simply became harder to manage.

As time went on, little displays of affection between the couple began to disappear. At night the space between them in bed widened; there were fewer showers together in the morning, fewer squeezes or pats on the rump while Mandy did the dishes, and Alan's occasional little surprise gifts came farther between. On the rare times when they both sat before the TV together, Alan would take to the easy chair rather than sit beside Mandy on the sofa. "My back's sore; have to stretch my legs out," he would rationalize. Mandy began to resent intensely the lessening of affection and what she considered the absolute absence of romance in their relationship.

To worsen the situation, she had always assumed Alan would realize her sexual needs and be there for her, even though she could never bring herself to mention it to him. There were several evenings when she put Stephanie to bed and soaked in a hot bubble bath, then dabbed Chanel No. 5 on her neck and between her breasts and thighs, even put on fresh make-up before slipping on a sexy nightgown. Only once—on the first occasion—did her efforts pay off, and then their love-making was wonderful. On her later tries, however, Alan wasn't interested. His excuses were lame and inconsiderate. He would claim, "I've had a hard day and have to get up early for the meeting tomorrow," or, "Oh no, not now. I had a couple of highballs after dinner and you know I can't perform when I've been drinking." Then there was the worn-out old standby, "I've got a headache." His transparent excuses merely added to Mandy's frustration and repressed anger. When Alan occasionally was in the mood for sex, he seldom cared about Mandy's satisfaction.

Once, impulsively, she bought a paperback romance—The Fires of Desire—at the corner store and began to read it while Stephanie napped during the day. Not quite a third of the way through it, she flung it to the floor in disgust. Fantasy it may have been, but how sad it was to read about other people's tender intimacy and steamy passion when she was robbed even of communication in her marriage, not to mention satisfying sex. The only pillow talk she and Alan engaged in consisted of the next day's agenda or errands that had to be done.

Increasingly Mandy found her moods swinging between a fairly even keel and a definitely negative downside. There seemed to be few positive highs to balance out the steadily declining tenor of her moods. But instead of expressing her needs to Alan—either physical or emotional—she would let things bottle up inside and fester until she would explode in hurt and frustration, often catching Alan by complete surprise.

On a Monday evening, Stephanie in bed, Alan sat fuming in silence before the TV set, watching the Maple Leafs being routed by the Philadelphia Flyers. Hoping to seduce her husband, Mandy casually waltzed into the family room in only her bra and panties just as a bench brawl erupted. Her timing, it seems, was terrible. Expecting her husband to chase her up to the bedroom and molest her with great passion, he only barked at her angrily: "Get the hell out of here and get some clothes on!"

Mandy recoiled in shock and, deeply hurt, shot back at him, "You big shit! Go ahead and watch your fucking hockey game. Shit!"

She ran, crying bitterly, to her room and fell onto the bed, hating to hear such words from her own mouth.

Little disappointments brought out a certain immaturity in Mandy; when things wouldn't go her way, she would pout childishly or fly into a rage, driving Alan to withdraw in anger into his study, a stiff drink in hand, to resume work until late in the evening.

There were moments of peace between them, for Mandy had become pregnant again. Two and a half years after Stephanie's birth, Mandy had reached the late stages of the term. But by this time, despite occasional truces, the marriage appeared to be in serious trouble. Alan, as usual, was always preoccupied with work and never saw Mandy's quiet apprehension, which had arisen from the difficulties associated with the first birth. And since he never thought to ask her about her feelings, Mandy assumed he didn't care.

She became sadder and more withdrawn as the days before delivery arrived. This wasn't the way she'd planned for her pregnancies. Surely there could be more togetherness. Without really being able to put her finger on any single cause, Mandy felt an emptiness that seemed to pervade her soul. She wondered if Alan still found her attractive—even with this huge, protruding belly. When she plied for compliments or even a small moment of attention, Alan quite bluntly told her he was put off by her little games, that she should grow up, be more mature. In short, it was crystal clear that he was becoming more and more disenchanted with Mandy and his marital situation.

Despite these stresses on the couple, they were thrilled to have a new baby boy, to complete their idea of the perfect family unit. But it had been just short of three years since Mandy experienced the terrible trouble with Stephanie's birth. And although Mandy was assured by the doctors that all would go well this time, she found herself praying often over the last few weeks for an easy and healthy delivery. Again the doctors seemed concerned only with her physical state, to the neglect of the emotional and the added stress on her body.

But little Stephen was born without undue difficulty, though again it had to be done by caesarean section. From birth he was a

110

difficult baby; Mandy thought that perhaps it was because he could feel the tension in the air. Stephen stayed awake more than most babies, particularly at night, when for some undetermined reason he would wail in discomfort until he was picked up and held or fed. Alan wouldn't budge from bed, so Mandy's sleep suffered as the weeks dragged on. She was constantly tired and irritable and became unreasonably demanding of everyone's time. Stephanie, too, felt the tension. She had become resentful of Stephen, of displacing her as the family focus. She therefore pulled every trick she could think of to get her parents' attention. And rather than try to work out solutions to the unrelieved tensions of these weeks and months, Alan would deliberately stay out after work for a drink several nights a week, just so he wouldn't have to face the confusion and the probable arguments that awaited him at home.

Each member of the family lived now in a completely different world, each with his or her own selfish perspective, unwilling to see or understand another's needs or viewpoints, no one realizing just how little they were sharing in the family any more. When Alan was home, he was quiet, introverted, busy with his studying or so caught up in his interests that he never seemed to feel Mandy's need for adult companionship or closeness. He was, after all, bringing home the bacon; he was doing his job and doing it well—providing a comfortable home for his family. Mandy, on the other hand, recognized that a comfortable home consisted of more than simply a shell with a roof and furniture and food, but she couldn't convince Alan of that. She found difficulty even putting her frustration into words that he could understand. In his view, she was being completely unreasonable. By God, he didn't even have parents! What was her problem? All she had to do was take care of the kids and the house. She had her work to do and he had his. His bottom line was, "Let's get on with it." And it was settled. He would talk about it no more.

Mandy began to resent Alan's days, filled as they were with meeting interesting people, occasional travel to new places, frequent luncheons, conferences and other business functions that were all a part of his work. Her life, on the other hand, was taken up with the dishearteningly mundane trivia of just keeping up with the house and children—changing diapers, cleaning, shopping, driving to doctors' appointments, potty training Stephanie and nursing Stephen. Alan's life outside the home looked so much more glamorous. It wasn't that Mandy disliked her role so much or even envied his; if only Alan could understand how frustrating her life was right now. If only he would offer to help relieve some of the burden, or at least allow her to escape with him once in a while to somewhere romantic, just the two of them again.

She started to believe that Alan's aloofness was somehow the result of her inadequacies. Perhaps something she'd done or something about her caused him to pull away so much. Once, for example, he remarked that a particularly important deadline was going to force him to work all weekend, and Mandy reacted by going off by herself and calling up every negative feature of herself that she could think of. Each one, in her view, was sufficient to cause Alan to make up some excuse to be apart from her. Never once did she attribute face value to Alan's explanation of his need to work. She finally decided that she was probably too fat for him; after all, she saw herself as having an ugly pear shape, with about twenty pounds still to shed from her pregnancy. Well, she could start her diet tomorrow. Today she was too tired and the children needed too much of her time and energy. And Alan didn't need her at all, so what was really the point of even starting a diet tomorrow?

All through this uncomfortable period in their marriage, Mandy still longed to have special, private times with Alan. She needed the intimacy and reassurance that he still loved her. But she felt constantly thwarted, terribly cheated of that time together. Even the children came between them, with their unrelenting demands for Daddy's attentions whenever he came through the door.

During the leisure times when the couple could have shared perhaps a quiet, private evening at home or a cozy dinner out, it always seemed that they had scheduled some social function with friends. Usually, of course, it was with Alan's friends, because of his need to "firm up the business connections." With them Mandy tended to be withdrawn, having little in common even with the wives. Not only did many of the company wives have their own jobs away from home, but most of the conversations focused on the company work, which she knew nothing about. Even the wives with other jobs knew much more about what the company was doing than she; Alan simply never spoke about it, so she felt lost at sea in the discussions. In addition, she still had an uneasiness around people with money and power. They seemed intimidating and uninterested in listening to anyone. To Mandy they seemed interested only in small talk, or their conversations centered on the company or on money and material possessions, with obtaining more money, more power.

Throughout this period Mandy experienced wholesale feelings of frustration, anger, and a complete range of others that she couldn't even identify. The emotions built slowly over time, swirling, churning, rushing through her unannounced and leaving criss-crossed trails of burnt-out feelings melting into each other. She had no choice but to go through them, no words to describe them, no ear to listen to her in any case. Mandy's moods and her marriage both seemed to be in trouble.

Chapter Twelve

Christmas, everyone hoped, was going to be fun that year. Stephen was almost two years old and Stephanie was almost five, and knew everything there was to know about Santa Claus. The plan was to visit the grandparents in Falmouth, and both Stephanie and Mandy were terribly excited about the upcoming holidays. Alan was busy with work, as usual, and little Stephen just wasn't quite old enough to know what was going on.

Mandy had bought a few gifts "from Canada" for the grandparents and was looking for a safe place to store them; the floor of Alan's closet seemed a logical place. She stooped to move several boxes that he'd stacked there and noticed a red envelope on the floor. Reaching to pick it up, she saw that it was a holiday greeting card. But what was it doing here? Opening it, she saw that it indeed was a Christmas card with a little note that someone had written. Mandy's body tightened with a chill as she glanced at the words. "Can't wait till Tues. darling. It's hard to wrap your gift. All my love, Diane."

She didn't want to look any further. The name Diane didn't register as anyone she knew. There was just a sudden pain, an overwhelming feeling of hopelessness. What should she do? Whom should she tell? Should she bring it up in conversation with Alan? Or should she wait till after Christmas? For the rest of the day she was in a dull fog, going through the motions of housework and caring for the children but not really being there. Alan caught her off guard by walking through the doorway early, his arms full of treats for everyone. The children ran screaming "Daddy, Daddy," to him. He looked so different to Mandy, so handsome in his three-piece tweed suit. He was relaxed, smiling in a way she hadn't seen for a long while. "You know, I'm really beginning to get into the spirit of the season," he said, beaming.

Mandy wondered if he saw her hurt. She tried to appear

cheerful, particularly when the children seemed so happy to throw themselves onto the carpet and rip open the delights that Daddy had brought home in the bags. "You shouldn't spoil them so," Mandy commented.

"Ah, Christmas comes but once a year," he said. "No harm in starting just a little early once in a while."

He made funny faces at the children as he playfully wound up the mechanical puppy which flipped and barked about on the table to their squeals of delight. "The poinsettia is beautiful," Mandy said rather emptily, trying to smile.

She silently wondered what he'd gotten for his Diane—and thought with terrible sadness about how he would welcome Diane's present to him.

Over the next few days Mandy happened to notice several changes in Alan. He was being ever so meticulous about how he got dressed for work in the morning. He always looked good in his clothes, but now he made sure his shirt, socks and tie were just right for the suit, and he had to have a matching silk handkerchief for his lapel pocket. His sense of color seemed to have taken on more flair, more panache. He also changed his after-shave lotion and began using a different toothpaste. Mandy started to blame herself: What did I do to cause him to do this? Where did I go wrong? How could I have been so blind?

Mandy felt so hurt and confused. She never thought Alan would or could have thought of being unfaithful. Maybe that was the problem; maybe she took their relationship for granted. She became angry. Who was this Diane? What was going on? She knew she'd have to confront Alan and do it now; the hurt was too deep.

That night she put the kids to bed early, feeding and bathing them before he got home. Alan was rather surprised to find the house so quiet; it was usually a madhouse at supper. Mandy even had wine with supper. In fact, she'd been sipping a bit while she cooked the dinner before he arrived, just to relax her thoughts.

But now somehow she wished she hadn't. Her face was flushed as it always seemed to be with alcohol.

"Where are the kids?" Alan asked, looking around.

"I fed them and put them to bed early," said Mandy. "They

seemed to be really tired this afternoon."

"Boy, I'm famished," he said. "I had to work through lunch today and haven't had a thing since breakfast except coffee and a stale bagel. What's for dinner?"

"Meatloaf. I picked up a bottle of wine to go with it."

"Smells great. Let me at it."

Mandy was unusually quiet during their meal, eating and sipping wine with only scattered comments on how the day went. Supper was almost over when Alan finally asked if something was wrong.

Not knowing just how to start, Mandy remained true to form—very spontaneous and reactive—and got right to the point, blurting it out.

"I'm sorry for snooping; I didn't really, but I found your Christmas card from Diane. I'm sure you've got an explanation, haven't you?"

Alan sat in shock, just staring at her. She went on.

"This must all be in my imagination, isn't it? Is this some kind of big joke or is there really someone else?"

Alan put down his fork and picked up his wine glass and tilted it back. He put it down and stared at the glass for a moment, then took a deep breath and started to explain. "Well, shit. I'd hoped to wait till after the holidays to tell you. But as long as it's here now..."

He paused again, wondering whether it was best to be blunt or try to soften the blow. He decided just to get the matter out.

"Well, yes, I'm sorry, there is someone else. It's no one special. You don't know her. I guess I've just had enough of marriage, or maybe I'm just mixed up. I don't know. It's just that things seem to be happening so fast—marriage, the kids, all the hassles of work, the whole thing. Things here just don't seem to be working out the way I thought they would. There's just too many problems. I need a break for a while. I think I need to get away for a while."

Mandy sat in a daze as he talked, her whole world crumbling around her. How could this be happening?

"My God," she said, "sure, we have problems, but why couldn't we have talked about them?"

"No, you couldn't have understood my problems," he replied,

his voice starting to rise in anger. "You don't know what my problems are! I don't even understand them myself."

He went on, still agitated: "My life at work's exciting, full of energy. It's fun, it's a challenge. Here at home it's no fun. You're too caught up in your world, with the kids. We're on two different planets. There's no way you can understand my needs."

"But why do you have to have another woman—or is it women? Why?"

"I just don't like to bring home any business problems," he said defensively. "I never know what to expect when I come in the door. I thought you wanted to work, have a career. I need to be around people in business, who're on their way up, not stagnating—not that you are, but shit, it's not just a sexual thing. She understands me, in a business sense. Oh fuck, I don't know how to say it."

More thinking out loud than addressing Alan, Mandy blurted, "But what are we going to do now? What's going to happen, then?"

It was then that she realized how completely in control of their situation Alan was. She sat there helpless, almost in shock.

"Well, maybe I should move out for a while," he said, and he picked up his glass and downed the wine.

"To be with her, I suppose!" Mandy screamed. Abruptly she pushed her chair from the table, turned and ran, crying, to their bedroom, as a swirl of emotion swept over her. She threw herself on the bed and sobbed, her world shattered. "My God, what am I going to do?" she kept asking herself over and over again. Alan stayed away. Her mind, unable to focus on the immediate problem, simply floated through the waves of emotions that now battered her. It was as if she were at sea in a small boat, being tossed and belted by a hurricane, and there was nothing to do but endure it. Then there came a time when she vaguely felt the tears streaming down her face and wondered how long she'd been laying there. It seemed that it must have been a few hours. She turned over onto her side, tried to put her feet on the floor and slowly made it to the bathroom. Without looking into the mirror, she turned on the faucet, wetted a facecloth and scrubbed the tears from her face. Then she took a deep breath and looked at herself in the mirror. There she saw a helpless little girl, homeless and lost, friendless, a victim of the world's whims. Nothing was left. She turned and walked from the room.

Alan had retreated quietly to his study. Just then Mandy couldn't find words to speak to him, so didn't knock or go in to him. But she just couldn't stand in front of his door like an old broom; she had to do something, so she decided to take a walk in the cold night air, as she often did when she needed to think.

This night was so different from the others. Under the clear sky the sharp December chill stung her cheeks and hurt her fingers; it worked its way through her coat and made her breath cloud up. But she didn't really feel the cold. What was she going to do? Who could help? She'd go home alone to Boston, making up some excuse for her parents. She had to be alone to think for a while. Was she a bad wife? Was it her housekeeping? Was there any good in her at all? So many foolish thoughts crept in.

After a few blocks she noticed the entrance to the little park behind their house and turned in. At the end of the winding little path she looked around and in the moonlight recognized the place where the children, especially Stephanie, loved to watch the squirrels and play. She started to cry again, remembering she wasn't the only one involved in the mess—they were too. They were still her responsibility, and she wasn't going to let anything happen to them. Oh, what where they all going to do? Turning her face up to the night sky, full of stars, she thought how peaceful it all looked. But the sky—and that peace—seemed so far away. Why couldn't life be that peaceful, she thought? She felt suddenly a need to pray. She couldn't remember the last time she did that, but who else could she turn to, but God?

"Help me, dear Lord. Oh, if you're really there, please Lord. Please show me what I have to do. I love Alan, and I want to be a good wife. Please take care of me and the children. There's nowhere else to turn. Please, dear Lord."

The sobs came again, and the chill on her cheeks began to sting. She wiped her eyes and pushed her hands deep into her coat pockets, hunching her shoulders. Then she turned and started back to the house, unaware of how that little prayer had already eased her mind.

During the next two days she worked almost ceaselessly to get the house in order and the children's things packed. She kept busy, pushing herself to do anything to keep the thought of Alan's leaving from her mind. Whenever she stopped, a flood of emotion would start to sweep over her like a tide, and she would dive again into some activity, trying to hum or sing—anything to keep the thoughts away. The more she was active, she reasoned, the closer she would be to Falmouth and the old security of home. Stuffing some of Stephen's clothes into a half-full diaper box, she suddenly straightened and said out loud, "Oh oh, I haven't called my folks!"

Dropping the handful of clothing, she immediately went to the phone and dialed, then plopped into the adjacent chair, suddenly feeling very tired from her work. After a few rings she heard her mother's voice on the other end of the line.

"Hello?"

"Hi, it's me," Mandy said, trying to control her voice. "I forgot to call you. We're getting ready to leave, but I've got some bad news. I'm afraid Alan won't be coming with us."

"Oh, that's a shame," Anne said. "Why won't he be coming? Is there something wrong?"

"No, nothing's wrong," replied Mandy. "It's just that he's been ordered to fly to San Francisco, or one of those towns across the bay. He has to oversee some new construction on one of those new malls, to make sure everything goes according to the design or something. I guess he has to stay there till after New Year's."

Mandy knew her excuse must have sounded quite lame, but she simply couldn't be more creative in explaining his absence.

"I'm sorry, dear," Anne said. "Well, ...are you sure everything's all right?"

"Yes, everything's fine. We'll be coming in on Eastern flight 152 at Logan on Tuesday, 9:30 in the morning. You don't have to be right there just then, because it takes at least twenty minutes or so to get through customs. So it'll be more like 9:45 or so."

"That's all right, dear," said Anne. "We'll be there at 9:30 just in case the plane comes in early."

"It'll be good to see everybody," Mandy said. "Give my love to Dad. I've got to go now; the kids are getting hungry."

"Well, we'll be sure to be there, dear," Anne repeated reassuringly. "Oh, it'll be so nice to have the family all together again.

And I can't wait to see my darling little grandchildren. You make sure they're bundled up, you hear? There's no snow yet, but it's bitter cold."

"I will, Mom. Don't worry about them. Kiss for Dad. 'Bye."

"'Bye, sweetheart."

Down the hall in their bedroom, Alan was packing some of his own things. He'd already found a condominium near their old apartment in uptown Toronto. Although it was a distance of only five miles or so, to Mandy it seemed a world away. Indeed, suburban Willowdale, though part of metropolitan Toronto and connected to it with unbroken urban development, was so different from the city that it seemed in another country. Even though she and the children would be gone for more than two weeks, Alan wanted to be out, to be away from the source of his discontent and nearer his work. He would be leaving after he dropped everyone off at the airport early in the morning.

It was nearly midnight when Alan came into the bedroom, following Mandy by some ten minutes. Thoughtlessly, he switched on a light and went to the radio to set the alarm. Too late he warned, "Cover your eyes."

Turning off the light he undressed to his shorts and got under the covers. Settling in on his back, he announced, "Damn it, I don't see why you have to be so damned childish as to run home to your parents like a little kid. That's stupid. When are you going to grow up?"

"It may be stupid, but what kind of Christmas would the kids have here?" Mandy replied softly.

Alan pulled in a deep breath and let it out noisily. He had to agree with her on the point but said nothing. It was true that he wasn't terribly concerned with how Mandy felt, but he didn't want to spoil this special holiday for the children. Rolling on his side away from her, he admitted, "Well, I don't want to ruin their Christmas."

At his comment Mandy also turned on her side, facing the edge of the bed. "How can you say that? Don't you know you've ruined their whole lives? Do you think Christmas even matters any more?" She pulled the covers over her face and wept silently, so she wouldn't provoke him further. Eventually they both slept.

At the airport ticket line Alan set down the suitcases and looked at Mandy and the children, standing on either side of her and clutching her hands. He said, "I'll get in touch with you in Falmouth in a few days."

He was very different this morning. His words were somewhat stiff and he appeared distant, yet his face betrayed a sadness in him. As he looked down at the children, tears glistened in his eyes. He knelt on one knee and took Stephen into his arms, then reached out for Stephanie and hugged them both. "Daddy loves you and hopes you have a nice time at Gramma's. We'll see you soon."

Mandy's heart was breaking with the pain she felt at that moment. Thank goodness she had the children to think about, to care for, she thought. It was the only thing that kept her going. She had to be brave for their sake.

Alan stood and briefly hugged Mandy, telling her, "Have a good flight. I'll get in touch. 'Bye, kids. Daddy loves you. Merry Christmas." Then he turned and walked through the crowd, back to the car.

Logan International Airport was less crowded than Toronto's, but the traffic seemed to be much thicker in Boston. Ralph became irritated rapidly. "How come all the world's worst drivers have to congregate in Boston?" he griped. "This is worse than when we came up."

"Well, dear," Anne offered, "You're just too used to traffic on the Cape. We'll be out of it in a little while."

The ride to Falmouth was uneventful, and Mandy had little to say. She was grateful that Anne sat in the back seat with the little ones and tried to keep up a running conversation with her grandchildren— mostly Stephanie—for much of the way. In front, Ralph was his usual quiet self on the road, except to bark occasionally at a rude driver or point out something unusual on the landscape. Beside him, Mandy leaned her head back against the seat cushion and let her eyes wander at the passing scenery of eastern Massachusetts. It was good to be coming home, but somehow it didn't seem like home any more—at least yet. Anne could sense that something was troubling Mandy, but credited it to Alan's absence or the flight over. Perhaps there would be time to talk about it later.

Brad met everyone at the door, giving Mandy and the children big hugs. Almost 22 by now, he seemed quite mature, and enjoyed immensely his status with the children as uncle. Mandy was surprised to remember that he was finishing his final year at University of New Hampshire as a geography major. "I'm specializing in physical geography—fluvial processes. You know—things like flooding and erosion and pollution. Our water supply needs all the help it can get," he explained.

"That's not the only thing that needs help," Mandy said, a trace of bitterness in her voice.

"What do you mean?" Brad asked.

"Oh, nothing." Mandy found herself in a situation where she didn't want to be. "They're cutting down all the forests and ruining the air too," she replied weakly. "Excuse me, I've got to go up and unpack some things for the kids."

Ralph disappeared into the living room with his morning paper. Anne, who had been watching Mandy from the kitchen, noticed her discomfort at the brief exchange with Brad. Wiping her hands, she poured Ralph a cup of coffee and took it to him. Then she turned to Brad. "Why don't you take the kids into the family room and read them one of those story books in the rack?"

Brad made a horrible face, hunched over and raised his arms in the air, clawing his hands in pretence of being a monster, to Stephanie's great delight but scaring Stephen badly. Brad quickly reverted to his avuncular demeanor and scooped up the children, asking, "How would my little niece and nephew like to hear the story of the goose that laid the golden egg?"

Stephanie squealed with delight, clapped her hands and screamed, "Yes, yes, Uncle Brad. Read us about the goose's egg!"

Brad carried them into the family room, plopped them down beside him and reached for the children's books.

With everyone thus occupied, Anne followed Mandy upstairs. She knocked softly on the door and walked in, to find Mandy sitting on the edge of the bed. The suitcases remained closed.

Anne sat beside her and rubbed her back slowly and lovingly. "What's the matter, sweetheart? Is there something we should talk about? Is it Alan?" she pried gently.

"Oh Mom," Mandy burst out, "everything's coming apart."

When her sobbing subsided, Mandy tried to explain what had taken place, to Anne's complete surprise. To her, they had seemed such an ideal couple, so wrapped up in each other. How could this have happened?

Christmas came and went with the traditional festivities—sumptuous dinners, the annual Passion Play put on by the Catholics at the high school, church on Christmas Eve, opening presents the following morning, calls to and from relatives and close friends, turkey dinner in the afternoon. By four o'clock on December 25, Christmas, for all practical purposes, was over. Everything had been done, and the Cartwright family, having had their fill of turkey and all the trimmings—as well as three kinds of pie—were stuffed and lazy. Both Ralph and Brad fell asleep in front of the TV, the children were put in bed for naps, and Mandy sat in the living room watching the snow begin to fall outside. Only Anne remained quietly active, having to clean up after dinner. The mood had changed. With no precise plans for New Year's Eve—except Brad, who planned to attend a friend's party—for the Cartwrights the holiday season had ended.

For several days after Christmas, Mandy moped around the house, scarcely speaking. Anne took over responsibility for caring for the children, because it was clear that Mandy was physically and emotionally exhausted. She would cry at the drop of a hat, and even the slightest noise or confusion irritated her, causing an unreasonable tongue-lashing for the unwitting offender. Both Ralph and Anne became seriously concerned about her.

On Thursday Anne called a friend, Murray Harding, who agreed to see Mandy on Monday. Anne explained to her that Murray was a psychologist and was very interested in talking to her. Murray had helped a lot of people, and if she would see him, it could only help. Mandy was uncomfortable with talking to a stranger, but she agreed. Like Brad's water, she too needed all the help she could get.

"Maybe you need a day off just by yourself, dear," Anne suggested. "Why don't you take my car and go for a drive?"

"That's not a bad idea, Mom."

Early on Saturday morning, therefore, Mandy put down her

coffee and kissed her mother on the cheek. "I really appreciate you watching the kids for the day, Mom. I'll try not to be too late. Don't worry."

"I'll get the kids up soon. I think we'll make some cookies this morning. There's plenty of gas, dear, but you be careful on the road," Anne cautioned. "There's lots of crazy people out there."

"I will. See you later."

With a deep sigh Mandy started the motor and eased the car onto the road, without the slightest idea where she was going. Then a thought occurred to her. Boston. Passing through Falmouth, she aimed toward Buzzard's Bay and the city, which, now that she'd thought of it, seemed to draw her like a magnet. For an hour she gripped the wheel, eyes straight ahead, foot on the throttle as the car sped along the highway.

She noticed the traffic gradually becoming thicker. Must be getting near the city, she recognized. At once confused, not really knowing where she was going, she decided to pull off the highway for a cup of coffee and to settle her nerves. She had to think.

Sipping the hot liquid and staring at nothing out the window of the roadside cafe, Mandy battled her feelings. It was wonderful to be free today, by herself, but waves of sadness kept welling up within her. Where was she going, not just here, but with her life now that Alan was gone? It had to be something true to herself, but who was she, anyway, really? She desperately wanted to feel a sense of roots, of belonging. Instead, she felt only guilt, for placing such a burden again on her parents, and confusion about what it really meant to be a single mother. What was happening to her?

Back in the car, Mandy still struggled with her feelings, with what she was going to do. When she eventually saw the skyline of Boston against the overcast day, she realized she'd have to decide at least what to do today in the city. She hadn't been back here since her last time with Brent, for that awful experience with that terrible woman. Then she remembered the New Year's Eve party, and turned the wheel toward Boston Commons. The lights and Christmas decorations, still up, reminded her of that night when Brent swept her off her feet with such passion. That was so long ago now, it seemed.

She glanced toward Beacon Hill, but decided to pass by,

remembering too much of that memory from the past. She just wanted to please herself today, to forget the pain. Spying Filene's Basement, quick flashes of the few times there with her mother went through her mind. She would go in. Circling the block twice, she finally pulled into an alley, just behind a truck that was illegally parked. Uncharacteristically, she thought, what the hell? It's only a parking ticket.

She remembered the times she and Anne would watch the great crowds of women frantically fight for the sale items, which were just tossed into big bins or hung on open racks on the floor. Women would try on clothes over their street clothes, or even hide behind two or three ladies while they changed clothes—right on the aisles. The place was always a madhouse, but it was ridiculous, almost dangerous, on special sale days.

Wandering aimlessly in the basement Mandy spied an assortment of porcelain figurines like the ones her grandmother had at her house. Oh, how she missed not having her grandmother to talk to— and her warm smiles and embraces. Why did she have to die? She meant so much to Mandy. Mandy just had to buy one of those figurines, one of a slender ballerina balanced on one leg and looking so regal, so strong. As a little girl she had always wanted to be a ballerina, but soon lost interest in classes, especially after Miss Collins said her hips were too heavy for her ever to be a good dancer. Taking the little statue in hand, she smiled as she walked over to pay for it.

No ticket, she recognized as she neared the car. Things can't be all bad. Starting the motor she let her mind wander again to how much she had gone through since she moved away to Toronto. Here, today, away from those problems for a while, she felt like a tourist, that she didn't belong. None of her friends were here. But she didn't have friends anywhere. Where would she live? She began to feel a sense of panic, and her head began to throb. She'd better find a place to eat. Spotting a sign for Durgin Park Restaurant, she headed there to take in another old tradition, New England clam chowder, one of her favorites as a girl. Whenever the family had come to Boston for the day, Dad had taken them there for supper—and Brent had taken her there, too.

At the top of the stairs she looked past the entrance of the restaurant, to the red-checkered tablecloths and white-aproned waiters rushing around the floor. Somehow, this place was too hectic today, but she went in and ordered a bowl of chowder, finishing it quickly. She felt awkward sitting alone, and a sudden feeling of homesickness fell on her. Roots. She longed to know the comfort of her grandmother's arms, of being a little girl again. She had to find her roots. Panic again mounted in her. Leaving well enough to pay for her chowder and a sizable tip, Mandy hurried from the restaurant and back down to her car.

Where did she leave the car? The Old North Church, she now saw, was nearby, but she hadn't seen it before. Trying to get her bearings, she stood confused on the street. Did I leave it over by the church? Then she remembered. It was in the lot in back of the restaurant. With a sigh of relief she squeezed into the car and inched it back from the cars tightly packed on both sides. Pulling out onto the street she noticed the Old North Church again and thought of its meaning. That was where someone hung two lamps, indicating the British were coming by sea, and then Paul Revere had ridden off into the night to warn the people.

Boston was filled with roots, with history. She would go to the wharf, where the Boston Tea Party took place, where Old Ironsides was still docked. The day was chilly and grey, with thick, dark clouds scudding low overhead.

She drove the short distance to the docks and, impossibly, found a parking space. Taking her ballerina figurine, she walked over to an ice cream concession on the wharf and ordered a pistachio. Then, sitting on a bench and looking at the carnival atmosphere, and the few people out on this dark day, she wondered why some people were smiling and others seemed so somber. Why did she love people so much? Why was she so interested in what they felt?

As she watched a couple walk by hand in hand, she wished that Alan had understood her. But did she even really understand what was deep in her own heart? She knew only that she had a deep love and caring for all mankind, especially in this place, where the birthpangs of the nation had taken place. She was becoming excited to be here, in such a historically significant place. Somehow, she was beginning to feel that she could now belong.

With her ballerina in hand she wanted to make one last stop. She just had to see the wharf where the Boston Tea Party took place. She knew it was nearby. Engrossed in her adventure, she walked on the pier toward the site. The heavy clouds, unbelievably, held their moisture so far, but the day had become quite dark, almost foreboding. The pier was almost deserted in the late afternoon.

As Mandy walked closer to the water, she felt increasing anxiety, a rush of adrenaline that made her heart beat faster. Should she be walking this dark pier alone? But she had a mission to complete. It didn't matter that she was alone; she wasn't frightened any more. She was being led toward a sort of destiny, toward her roots.

Near the edge of the wharf, over the water she noticed the flickering of lights floating along the surface of the bay. By now she didn't really know where she was, except that this was a cobblestone walkway running along an open wharf area. There was no sign that said where she was, or where she was headed. And no one was nearby to ask. Stopping, then moving toward the edge of the dock, she looked out over the inky water and across the harbor to see piers and what looked to be storage warehouses. She leaned over the wooden railing that separated the wharf from the cobblestone walkway and stared at the water below, watching it lap up under the piles holding up the wharf. The water was perhaps twelve feet below her.

Tears welled up from within and rolled down her cheeks. What was she to do? From somewhere a message came to her, stirring her to move closer to the edge. All she had to do, said the message, was let go, just fall into the water, just float off that wharf, and all the pain and sorrow in the world would be gone. Feeling strangely strong, Mandy thought she was receiving glimpses of knowledge and wisdom, and these made her shiver with excitement. What did all this mean? She hesitated, trying to step back from the edge, but the message got louder, insisting that she had the power to change the world. All she had to do was fly off this wharf and the world would see what she had seen moments before. It sounded so wonderful—a world full of peace and harmony. And she could make it happen. She took a step toward the edge, almost involuntarily, as if she were being drawn. She moved closer, and the message boomed in her head. Save the world, fly off, you can do it! The water loomed up before her, beckoning her to join with it, to bring peace and harmony, to restore her roots.

Roots! Stephen and Stephanie! Leave them? No! She loved them. She thought of Alan and the love for him and the children that she carried within herself. It would all be gone. Suddenly the words that Linda Harney had spoken to her at school came back: "We've all got a place here. God loves me, and he promised in the Bible that if I just believe in Jesus and trust in him to solve any problem, he'd never leave me. He can handle anything that troubles me. All I have to do is ask him into my heart and trust that he'll give me whatever I need to overcome it."

Mandy wasn't sure of the exact words, but the sentiments she remembered clearly. Gathering her strength, she thought of the little ballerina in her hand. If I can just trick this voice inside me, she figured, and though weakened, she managed to toss the little figurine over the railing and into the water. "Here, this will take my place," she said, and fell backwards to the safety of the walkway.

She wanted to live. "Oh yes, God, I want to live," she said. "Thank you, God," this time whispering. "I trust that you can help me win, and I trust you. Just please give me a chance."

At that moment there was a hand on her shoulder and a commotion overhead. A man and woman were leaning over her asking if she was all right. Trying to smile, she attempted to reassure them that she had only fallen, that she just got a little dizzy. Helping her over to a bench, they waited with her a few minutes and then, assured that she was in control of herself, they went about their business.

Mandy sat there for another ten minutes, wondering what had happened, and becoming frightened at what she'd almost done. Oh God, I really need you now, she pleaded. Please help me to have my whole family back. Please, God.

Making her way finally back to the car, she drove off shakily. Not until she was on the southeast expressway did she begin to feel more relaxed and comfortable to be heading home. She stopped at a restaurant to call her mother, to reassure her that everything was okay, and that she would be home soon.

On the road again she wondered, had she really tried to kill herself? What were those feelings of being led? No one would understand if she tried to explain—she didn't understand any of it herself. She vowed never to tell anyone.

Chapter Thirteen

After breakfast on Monday morning, Anne drove Mandy over to Mr. Harding's office, situated in a beautifully renovated old Colonial house at the edge of downtown Falmouth. The low sign on the snow-covered lawn read "Murray G. Harding, Family Psychologist." Inside, in the reception area, the receptionist sat at a lovely old oak roll-top desk beside a long, antique table with an inlaid black leather top. Even the file cabinets were oak. Softly patterned, velvet easy chairs and other comfortable furnishings made waiting a pleasant, relaxing experience. "If you'll be seated, Murray will be with you momentarily," said the receptionist, smiling amiably.

Mandy was surprised at her use of Mr. Harding's first name. That must be to make us relaxed with him, she decided.

In a few moments Murray Harding walked through lace-curtained French doors off to the right, and smiled at Anne and Mandy. "Well, it's good to see you, Anne," he said with genuine warmth, shaking her hand. "And this must be Mandy. Delighted to meet you."

He offered his hand, which Mandy took hesitantly.

"Anne, would you like to have coffee while Mandy and I have a little talk? Betty will show you where it is. Come into the living room, Mandy. We've just remodeled it, and maybe you could let me know how you like it."

Turning to Anne he said, "We'll be a little while. Make yourself at home. Look around." He was distinctly proud of the renovations done to the old house.

Together they went through the French doors into the living room, a comfortably appointed study with another old desk, a wall of books and several oversized easy chairs on a thick carpet. There were also two long sofas. Murray led her to two easy chairs, close together at a ninety-degree angle. Mandy's chair faced the center of the room, at a wall curiously lacking any adornment, but simply painted in an offwhite color.

"Well, how do you like the room, Mandy?" he asked.

"It's nice. Very comfortable."

"I hope you'll feel relaxed here," he said with a smile. "Your mother tells me you've been under a lot of stress lately. I know a little bit about stress and might be able to help lighten your load, if you'd care to tell me a bit about it. Is there anything you'd like to tell me about that?"

Mandy didn't quite know where to start, nor did she feel comfortable even in telling this man anything. But she knew she had to if she was to put her life back together—only not everything.

He paused, waiting. After what seemed the longest time, Murray asked, "Mandy, how do you feel about your husband?"

Suddenly she brought her hands to her face and broke down in tears. "I love him. I love him," she said through her hands. From somewhere Murray produced a facial tissue which he offered to her. Drying her eyes Mandy continued, "I can see why he'd leave me. I've been terribly unattractive these past few months. I've been spending too much time taking care of the kids and cleaning house. I've let myself go. He's so busy with his work, and I haven't wanted to concern him with everything that needs to be done around the house. But sometimes it's just too much. The kids came too close—less than three years apart—and sometimes I just feel overwhelmed. And I think some of it's because of the problems I had with my first delivery."

As she talked the psychologist occasionally smiled and nodded his understanding. She continued describing what she thought might have contributed to Alan's leaving, and Murray listened patiently, his eyes always watching her. She said nothing of wanting to jump into the water of Boston Harbor. When Mandy could think of nothing more to say, Murray rose from the chair and stretched his hand to her, apparently wishing her to get up as well.

"Your life as a young mother isn't out of the ordinary," he tried to reassure her. "Many young women go through the same kinds of problems, even with their husbands finding another interest and leaving them. Almost all of these women make it through, but most of them have legal help to do so. I'd suggest that you might wish to seek some legal help. But most importantly, I'd strongly urge that you consider additional counseling, because I sense that you still have some anger to get rid of."

At that point Mandy became defensive. "I don't feel angry," she said. "Just sad."

She tried to smile. Inside she had become angry at this Murray's stupid and irrelevant conclusions. She knew the real problem, though she kept it to herself: I've failed as a wife. Alan only did what was natural under the circumstances. He's a wonderful husband and provider. He loves me but he doesn't like my immaturity. He wants an independent, self-sufficient and loving wife. And I've failed him.

In short, she was willing to blame herself for everything.

At this point her mind stopped roaming and she tried to focus again on the psychologist's words.

Smiling, she said, "Thank you so much for your time. But I think all I really need is a good rest."

Again, in her mind she was saying, When I have a chance to talk to Alan again, I'll just say I understand. Everything is all right. Now let's see if we can try again.

In her heart Mandy was convinced that if she only changed, she could win Alan back.

Murray accompanied Mandy through the French doors and into the reception area. Anne stood up, clearly apprehensive. But that soon disappeared in the face of the smiles she saw. The psychologist mentioned to both women that he'd recommended some further counseling for Mandy. Also, he thought it best that Mandy make an appointment with the family doctor to get some anti-depressant medication and some sleeping pills, because he too was concerned that she indeed needed some rest.

Mandy was encouraged by his last statement; he had actually agreed with her. Disregarding virtually all of his comments but the last, she went away uplifted from the visit, now thoroughly convinced her marriage would work out.

Oh, everything was going to be so good. God was going to teach her how to be a good wife. Over the next week she devoted hours every day reading at the library—anything she could find about personal relationships, intimacy, creating a lasting marriage. It was as if she wanted to absorb every bit of knowledge available. She made it a point to visit the Catholic church down the way every day for a quiet meditation. It felt as if God were guiding her now. She was sure that if she prayed hard enough and did as she was guided, Alan would love her again. That was her greatest desire. She really did love being his wife, and she wanted her family intact. Perhaps they had both just taken too much for granted until now.

Mandy was growing stronger physically as well. She started her mornings earlier and began taking active interest in the children's schedule. She began to notice just how much she'd allowed her mother to take over caring for the children and felt ashamed. Now, however, things would be different. She was their mother and must resume her responsibilities with them.

Anne and Ralph felt relieved that Mandy seemed to come alive again. To them, her interest in study and her hunger for spiritual things were healthy signs. Brad had returned to U.N.H. shortly after the holidays. The grandparents were pleased to have Mandy home, and now that she was in control, they began to pull into the background and let mother be in charge of her children. Then, in true grandparently fashion, they started wanting to spoil their grandchildren. Indeed, life among the Cartwrights took on a semblance of normalcy, and the grandparents were quick to praise both the children and their mother whenever an occasion arose.

But Ralph and Anne kept some of their thoughts about Mandy to themselves. They knew that her visit couldn't be permanent and were concerned about how Mandy would manage afterwards with two young children to care for alone. Ralph, particularly, felt hurt and angry toward Alan for what he'd done, but couldn't show Mandy his feelings, especially now that she expressed such love and optimism.

Alan hadn't called even once, however. Mandy reflected on the matter and concluded that he really should call because no one actually hated Alan. He'd been quite wonderful in light of all the problems she'd given him. Everyone was just too shocked to know what to do. But wasn't he concerned for his family? Why didn't he phone?

Alan did call, unexpectedly, two weeks after Christmas. The children were splashing together in their bath when the call came.

"I'm awfully sorry to call while the kids are in the bath," he apologized. "But how was I to know?"

"It's okay," said Mandy. "Just let me run in and get them. They'll be terribly disappointed if they don't speak with their father. Hang on just a second."

Mandy banged the phone down on the dresser, rushed into the bathroom and swooped a wide-eyed and open-mouthed Stephanie from the tub, trailing a stream of water to the bath mat. She grabbed a big towel and wrapped it hurriedly around the little girl and carried her back to the phone. "Mom, dry off Stephen and bring him to the phone, will you?" she yelled back over her shoulder. "Daddy wants to talk to Stephen."

Mandy plunked Stephanie down on the top of the dresser, still wrapped in the towel. "Here's Daddy. Say something to him."

"Hi Daddy," Stephanie said into the phone.

"Hi sweetheart, how's my little girl?"

"Fine."

"I'm sorry I couldn't be there with you for Christmas. What did Santa bring you?"

"Oh Daddy, Santa brought me a Barbie doll with a nurse's kit and a red tricycle with a bell that really rings and a basket and a Gaylord dog that walks on the floor and..."

After an abrupt, brief pause she suddenly asked, "Daddy, when are you coming home?"

"Just as soon as I can, sweetheart. But I don't know when that will be. I'm glad Santa brought you such nice things. Is your mother there?"

"Yes. Here's Mommy, Daddy. 'Bye, Daddy."

"'Bye, sweetheart."

Listening with Stephanie on the earpiece, Mandy sensed that Alan clearly wanted to speak with his children, but his voice sounded so distant and reserved.

Mandy took the phone and said, "Stephen wants to speak with you. Here he is."

Stephen grabbed the phone with both hands and strongly

pulled the mouthpiece right up to his face and simply yelled "Daddy, Daddy" over and over into the phone. There was little his father could say to interrupt him. Eventually Mandy took the phone and asked Gramma to escort the kids out of the room and into their nightclothes.

"Hi again," said Mandy, terribly pleased to be speaking with her husband after such a long time. "I'm so glad you called." She thought she heard Alan sigh—was it from impatience or something else?

"I've been doing a lot of thinking," he said.

"So have I."

Her voice became excited. She couldn't contain herself any more. The tears started to come and she blurted out, "I'm so sorry, Alan, and I want to make it up to you for being a rotten wife. I understand now why it was so easy for you not to want to come home. I've learned so much here, and God's answered my prayers."

On the other end of the line Alan almost winced at this outburst of emotion. "I'm sorry to have upset you, Mandy. Maybe I shouldn't have called right now."

"Oh no, Alan, I'm so glad you called. I'm sorry for rambling on. What did you want to say?"

"I'm sure your folks hate me by now," he said. "But I've had a lot to think about, and that's why I haven't phoned till now. The company's decided to move me to Vancouver for an important project, and I think we have to make some decisions. We have a lot to talk about."

"Oh Alan, I love you, and I want to come home."

"Well, go ahead and reserve some tickets," he said.

"I'll call you when I've made plane reservations. Can you meet us?"

"Sure. Let me know the details." He paused briefly, then said, "I've missed you all. Have to run now. Take care."

She was about to tell him how thrilled she was to have the family together again, how much she wanted to be with him, when she heard the phone click on his end. "'Bye, lover," she said to the buzzing phone.

"I've missed you all..." His last words still rang in her ears. She put the phone down and threw her arms in the air, terribly excited.

This call must mean that he still loves her! Thoughts tumbled quickly. What did he want to do? Whatever it was, he evidently wanted his family with him. Oh, thank you, God. Mandy was overcome with joy as she ran to tell her parents the good news. On the stairs she briefly remembered the other woman—she hadn't even thought to ask about her. But he'd called! He's missed us, and he wants his family back, so that must mean there's no other woman any more. She skipped down the last stairs and into the family room with the news.

Ralph and Anne accepted the story suspiciously and only reluctantly watched her and the children pack to leave, but Mandy was determined now to do everything in her power to save this marriage. From now on she would stand on her own two feet. She didn't blame her parents for their caution, for loving her so much; she knew that they were worried only because they wanted the best for her and the children.

The grandparents, still concerned, watched Mandy usher Stephen and Stephanie onto the ramp to board the plane, her tote bag almost dragging the floor under the weight of the children's paraphernalia. Stephanie clutched tightly the bag of treats that Anne had given her just before leaving for the airport. Leaning forward to kiss her mother and father, Mandy promised to call and let them know what was happening. Then she turned and marched the children through the turnstile, glancing back at the doorway to throw her parents a last kiss.

As the plane took off Mandy glanced quickly out the window then grabbed the children's hands in excitement. They were entranced with their surroundings and all the little things in the seat compartment to keep them occupied. Mandy leaned back in her seat, shut her eyes and breathed a deep sigh in anticipation of what lay ahead.

Chapter Fourteen

The disembarkation area at Toronto International seemed like a madhouse. It was incredibly crowded. From the milling swarm of people a cacophony of foreign languages met the ear. Mandy pushed the luggage cart before her, each child grasping the cart's curved handle. She carefully worked her way around tight groups of people, craning her neck to catch a glimpse of Alan. Finally she spied him, standing against a piling and peering over heads to find her. "There's Daddy," she announced excitedly to the children. Squealing with delight, they ran ahead and leaped into their father's open arms.

Alan looked much thinner but as handsome as ever, Mandy thought. She smiled as she approached him. He tried to smile back but there was a hint of reserve which made her a little nervous and undecided about what to say. "Hi. Thanks for meeting us," she finally said. Alan put an arm around her neck and gave her a little hug and a quick kiss on the cheek, then reached down and picked up the bags and started to work through the crowd to the parking area.

The ride back to Willowdale was full of meaningless chit-chat about the holiday traffic, Toronto's atrocious winter weather and how the children enjoyed Christmas. Stephanie did her best to steal the show, interrupting virtually every sentence the adults spoke. Stephen, now cranky, was clearly hungry and sleepy. Thus it was quite some time later that evening before Alan could feel comfortable about telling Mandy his plan.

Finally, the children asleep, with goblets of wine Alan and Mandy retired to the living room, where he laid out the situation. He was finished with the girl at the office. It had been a foolish thing to do, but now it was over and he didn't want any more said about it. What was more important was that he'd been transferred to Vancouver; this was a once-in-a-lifetime opportunity and he wanted her to come along with the kids. They'd be there for probably a year and then they would transfer back to Toronto and buy a bigger house. At that time, Charles Sumner had promised, Alan would be brought into the firm as a full partner.

He made it sound so exciting. Mandy could see how thrilled he was at the prospects, about moving upward. But the move to Vancouver had to be done fast if he decided to accept.

"When would we have to go?" Mandy asked, reluctant but trying to be as positive as Alan about the situation.

"I have to be there within the month," he said. "And I'd like to put the house up for sale right away. If it's not sold by the time I leave, you can sell it, then follow me with the kids. Just try to get a good price for it, but let the agent handle the details. Just keep me informed by phone of what's happening."

Mandy's head was so full; so much was happening all of a sudden. It was so much to absorb. She couldn't find the right words to say, and her long silence made Alan uncomfortable.

"Well, what are you thinking?" he pressed.

"I really don't know. It's all so fast. I guess I'm just bewildered by everything just now."

In truth, Mandy wasn't convinced that he even really loved her any more, and the thought of packing up to go to another strange place frightened her. But she didn't want to scare him away or appear to be negative. Besides, a wife was supposed to follow her husband anywhere his career took him, wasn't she?

"I guess I can adjust all right," she finally added. "I think it'll be exciting. But..." she paused, "what about us? It just seems that we have some problems to sort out, don't we?"

Alan quickly became defensive. "Look. That other situation is over and done with, and the best thing either of us can do is forget about the whole thing. There's no sense even thinking about it. Let's get on with the show, eh?"

"But do you love me?" Mandy had to ask. She sat next to him, vulnerable, needing her man, needing reassurance. Somehow she still felt insecure. He looked at her for a long while, then lifted his hand and brushed the hair from her cheek.

"I love you," he said. "Come on upstairs. I'll show you how much." For the first time in a long time, Alan made her feel like a

138

woman who was loved.

The next days went by quickly for everyone. Mandy's hope for rekindled romance went on the back burner because other matters took urgent priority. Packing, selling the house, and moving had to be done—quickly. And in the midst of the hubbub, the children needed care. Alan put the townhouse up for sale. In the middle of January the market wasn't as active as they'd have wished, but they hoped that with all their work on the interior, perhaps it would sell quickly nevertheless.

One night Mandy phoned her parents to say that she and Alan were going to try again. Clearly, Ralph and Anne were reluctant to see their daughter moving to Vancouver for the year; in their view matters were still unresolved. However Mandy tried to reassure them, her mother remained worried, Mandy could tell. On the phone she found herself in tears from her parents' distrust of Alan and the situation, which deeply hurt Mandy. She tried to hide the hurt in her voice, not wanting her family to think she couldn't work things out this time. She wanted so desperately to be grown up about everything. Sure, there were drawbacks to moving, but wasn't all of life an adventure despite the occasional drudgery or setback? Anne tried to be supportive, but Mandy knew she was hiding her true feelings of concern. She urged Mandy to call in a few days. Ralph said she was making a very uncomfortable bed that she'd have to lie in and wished her well with the drudgery of packing. All three were tense when they hung up.

Mandy hated packing. It represented the tearing up of roots. It also led to the old familiar insecurities about the unknown. And it could be backbreaking work. She did her best to look at the bright side of packing alone—Alan had to spend his spare time at the office to close up all loose ends—but after a short while she began to tire easily, having to plop into whatever chair happened to be handy. She also started to become ambivalent about making even small decisions and left them, as much as possible, for Alan. And when she missed Stephen's checkup at the doctor's office, Alan finally asked her if she was all right.

"Oh sure, I'm fine. Just a little bushed. It's okay."

As the days of activity moved by quickly, Mandy noticed that she'd lost a few pounds, likely because of all the bending and running up and down stairs carrying things—and on top of that, trying to keep the house clean for potential buyers. She'd also been eating less, being more preoccupied with the move. She decided to start an official diet to become even slimmer, to be more attractive to Alan—and perhaps therefore be better equipped to hold on to him, just in case. Losing weight, she discovered, was really much easier than she'd expected, no doubt due to her non-stop, almost frenetic urge to pack everything herself. By the time Alan had to leave for Vancouver, she was ten pounds trimmer.

For their last evening together, they hired a babysitter and went out to dinner, to relax together, to talk and plan. Mandy was glowing and her radiant smile was back. Alan was enchanted with the apparent changes he saw in her. She had changed. She was really pitching in with the move, and she'd been very understanding about not bringing up his activities of the past few months. He was encouraged and looking forward to a fresh start in Vancouver. The evening was perfect; they even danced for a while. Mandy felt a little tipsy with the wine, but Alan thought she was cute, and it made her all the more desirable.

They made love that night and were convinced, as they lay in each other's arms, that the past was truly behind them. The morning would bring the start of a new life for everyone even if they did have to be separated again for a short time. But the morning brought things that no one bargained for.

Mandy awoke early feeling very jittery, as if she were full of energy, even though it was well after midnight when the couple had finally fallen asleep. She bounded out of bed and made a big breakfast of bacon and scrambled eggs, pancakes and fresh fruit while Alan was taking his shower. While she finished her preparations, Alan, in his bathrobe at the breakfast table, went over the list of last minute details with her—what to do with the realtor, moving companies, their bank accounts, the utility companies and the like. As he covered each item, he would look up to make sure it had registered with Mandy. He noticed something of a far-off look in her eyes, and twice he'd had to repeat himself to see if she was listening. She seemed a trifle strange, with a wooden, almost robotic smile on her face, which wasn't natural for her. Alan chalked it up to his leaving—she didn't want him to leave and no doubt was just nervous and trying to hide her feelings.

He too was feeling a bit anxious, but this thing had to be done. His whole future depended on it. He didn't mind having to go to Vancouver but disliked having to relocate the whole family, and he still had nagging doubts about whether things would work with Mandy. Sure, the past few weeks had been great, and he really had missed the children when they were in Falmouth, but still... He brushed off his wave of doubt as the cab pulled up to the driveway. He dragged the last of his bags to the curb as the driver loaded the trunk for his ride to the airport.

Mandy and the children wouldn't be going with Alan to the airport. The couple had thought it best not to make a big production of leaving at the airport. Besides, it would have taken twice as long to get ready if the kids had had to be bundled up and taken outside in the early February cold. Alan kissed Stephanie and Stephen and gave them both bear hugs. He stood and put his hands on Mandy's shoulders to kiss her goodbye, and again he noticed something strange about Mandy's look. She seemed to be staring right through him.

He promised to phone from Vancouver later that evening, once he got settled. He would be looking for an apartment or house for them all, but the firm had arranged for him to connect with a realtor, so he wasn't too concerned at this point.

As the cab drove out of the driveway and onto the street, Mandy, still smiling broadly, waved back to Alan. The cab picked up speed and she watched it speed away. Then she immediately glanced at her watch—9:30. Oh good, she thought, the stores in the mall will be opening by now. Alan was gone. She might never see him again. Perhaps the plane would crash. Did he take his golf clubs from the garage? Abruptly her mind switched to things at hand. "Well, today should be a special day," she said out loud. Turning into the house she called, "Come on, Stephanie, Stephen. Let Mom help you dress. We're going to have a treat today."

She went into her own room and began looking through her closet for just the right outfit. Three sweaters lay on the bed, along with a discarded pair of slacks. It felt so nice to have things too big for a change. She would buy a new wardrobe now that she was slimmer.

Skipping down to the kitchen, she quickly glanced around. None of the food from breakfast was put away yet, and dishes were still all over the counter, normally a state of affairs that Mandy couldn't tolerate. But today, she thought to herself, these can wait. This is a treat day.

She bounced into the family room and turned off Sesame Street, much to Stephanie's displeasure.

"Oh Mommy, do we have to?"

"Yes, we do. We're going out today. This is a treat day for us," Mandy replied with a wide smile.

"Where are we going?" asked Stephanie.

"We're going to the mall. Mommy's going to be really good to you today. We're going to make this a party day so you won't be sad that Daddy's gone."

Mandy felt as if she had to surround herself with activity, with music and people who were doing things. She bundled up the children and whisked them out to the car. When the motor started, she turned on the heater and flipped the fan switch all the way on. It was a cold morning, and the fan blew only frigid air through the car, as the engine was still cold. Then she turned on the radio and flipped the dial back and forth to find just the right song. As she listened, she thought she heard the radio giving her hidden messages, something she hadn't noticed before.

She strained her ears but the messages weren't clear yet. That was all right; soon they would make more sense. How wonderfully exhilarated and full of energy she felt. She eased the car out of the driveway and headed toward Yorkdale Shopping Centre.

All day they wandered around the mall, stopping into stores and browsing through shelves and racks. One of the first things Mandy bought was a stroller for Stephen to ride in; it hadn't taken him long to become cranky about having to drag along beside his mother. Soon afterward Stephanie complained of being hungry, and the trio stopped for an early lunch. But for some reason Mandy didn't feel like eating. She shared Stephen's ice cream cone but felt impatient to get back into the stores.

She moved through the aisles deliberately, as if looking for something in particular, as if there had to be a pattern to her search.

142

She couldn't miss what she was looking for, though she couldn't quite put her finger on what it was. Stephanie lagged behind, having the freedom to search the shelves as well—with her mother occupied—and Mandy would have to call back to her. "Stay with me, Steph. We'll pick up something else to eat in a little while."

Stephanie actually had little problem keeping up with her mother, as every so often Mandy would stop and take some item in her hands. Stephen seemed to enjoy being pushed around, and with his stomach satisfied, it wasn't long before he was asleep.

Mandy became more intense in her search. She picked up various things—brass candlesticks, a figurine of a dancing girl, a small desk lamp—and she would feel them all over, as if to sense that their vibrations were good. Certain colors attracted her—blues, orange, and white—and she would move to whatever it was and pick it up to examine it carefully. Twice she passed by the same store and glanced at a window full of stuffed animals. Suddenly she felt led to go in and buy a white, stuffed unicorn almost two feet tall that sat up in the corner of the window. When the saleswoman returned the credit card, she asked if the unicorn was for one of the children's birthdays. Mandy turned as she strolled happily out of the store, answering, "This is going to be mine forever and ever."

By five-thirty Stephanie clearly had had enough of wandering around the mall. Mandy had overindulged both children with lunch at McDonald's, ice cream sundaes and candy treats, and a bag full of little toys for each of them. What more could they ask? But when Stephanie finally sat down on the concrete floor and screeched uncontrollably, Mandy realized it was time to go home.

She looked for an exit to the parking lot and headed outside. But by this time she had no idea where the car was parked. It took another forty minutes of wandering through the huge lot to finally locate the car. Nor did Mandy remember to ask how to fold up the stroller, and so, rather than try to figure it out, she simply left it beside the car as she drove off, feeling especially magnanimous about her anonymous gift to some shopper. It occurred to her that if everyone were to do something like that every day, what a world this would be!

Seated behind the wheel, Mandy noticed that her senses were especially reactive, almost over-sensitive. Lights and sounds came to her with almost exquisite sharpness. Despite the chilling temperature outside, she was becoming very warm, too warm. Beads of sweat appeared on her forehead, and her hands felt clammy in the gloves. Her heart pounded and adrenaline pumped through her body. Mind racing, her thoughts, coming quickly, started to overlap, to tumble into one another. She had trouble focusing properly and became concerned that she might not be able to drive home safely. And it was dark, which only increased her apprehension. She checked to make sure the children were securely fastened in their seat restrainers. Blinking often to regain focus, she drove slowly, carefully, taking side streets rather than the main highway, with its swooshing, menacing traffic.

To her huge relief she finally turned onto the road that led to Century Crescent and home. Breathing a great sigh, she turned off the key and undid the fastenings on the children's belts.

"Okay, kids," she said enthusiastically, "let's get in and have something to eat."

Yes, she would tuck everyone safely inside tonight and light a cheery fire in the fireplace. After a light supper for the youngsters—peanut butter sandwiches and cocoa—she let them play in the family room with the TV on. She wasn't hungry at all and just munched on a Mars bar she'd picked up that afternoon. Then she went to take a hot bath, but her attention became diverted on the way: it wasn't right that some of the corners of the house were dark. Tonight should be cheery and pleasant—it needed to be bright inside on this dark night. As she went from room to room and down the halls, she turned on each of the lights. In the kitchen she switched on the radio—it was too quiet there.

Upstairs in the bedroom she turned on another radio and in Alan's study the stereo, forgetting that speakers went on also in the family room. Soon every light in the house was on, and the sounds of several radio and TV stations vied antagonistically with one another. Mandy saw no problem with the competing noises; it was all right. Nor was she really aware that all the lights were on, in fact, that all of this was quite out of the ordinary.

Feeling pumped full of energy, Mandy's body felt as if life were speeding around and around through her veins. She couldn't stop the racing feelings, nor did she even want to. Her body seemed to be pumping adrenaline faster and faster while thoughts flitted in and out of her mind in no clear order.

Suddenly she remembered the children's bedtime and quickly went downstairs to turn off the TV. "All right, kids," she said loudly and firmly, clapping her hands. "It's time for bed. Come on. Mommy will read you a story. Let's go. Time for beddy-bye." She picked up Stephen and carried him upstairs, changed his diapers and hustled him into his nightclothes while Stephanie got hers on. Then she took them into her own bedroom, where they scrambled up onto the master bed. Bundling them on either side of her, she read them stories about Goldilocks, George and the Dragon and twice through Rapunzel—it was a story she particularly liked. They snuggled close against mother and listened raptly, and at the end of the second round she slapped the Rapunzel book closed and smiled brightly. "Okay, that's it. Lights off."

She tucked the little ones in and hugged them both. It seemed so right to have them sleep with her in the big bed tonight. After all, this was a special treat day. They loved the stories Mommy read to them and happily fell off to sleep dreaming of dragons and fairy queens, unaware that anything was wrong with their mother. Nor did they say anything when she walked out of the room leaving the light on.

Downstairs Mandy lit a fire in the fireplace. The dancing flames made the whole room glow, which somehow frightened her. Thoughts of Hallowe'en and Ichabod Crane and the Headless Horseman skitted through her mind. The world she normally experienced was being pushed aside, intruded upon and rearranged by her out-of-kilter thoughts.

Mandy was larger than life now. She flitted from one activity to another with more energy than she'd had in a long time. She went from room to room looking for things to do. She was picking up the toys in the family room when she noticed the fire dancing in the fireplace. It seemed to beckon her. Standing straight up, she stared into the flames, troubled by them. Then she thought, perhaps if she fed the fire it wouldn't bother her any longer. She suddenly noticed her stuffed unicorn in the corner. She went to it and picked it up. Holding it close to her face with both hands, she moved closer to the glowing fire and seemed to stare through it to a far-off place with no more hurt and pain. She leaned down and held out the unicorn, but before it reached the flames, she was startled by the ringing of the phone. I'll do this afterwards, she decided.

It was Alan.

"Oh Alan, I'm so happy you called."

He seemed so far away. His voice felt good, and it seemed what she needed—so strong, but oh, so distant.

"I'm sorry to be calling so late. It must be eleven back there. You're still awake?"

Mandy had no conception of the time, and simply said, "Yes."

She felt terribly confused and vaguely remembered—with a sudden sense of guilt—what she was going to do with the unicorn.

Something within her wanted to cry out to Alan about how strange she felt, but something else warned her that it wasn't a good idea; he might reject her and wouldn't want to be with her. She wasn't sure that she even wanted to be with herself tonight.

"The flight was okay. No problems with the weather—there's only a slight drizzle here. I'm staying at Hotel Vancouver." He gave her the room and the phone number, which she jotted on a paper lying on the desk.

Good thing he didn't ask what she'd done for the day, she thought to herself.

"I'll be going out with the realtor tomorrow," he continued. "You're really going to love the scenery. Even in the winter it's beautiful here, with the ocean and the mountains. And there's no snow, except on the mountains. We can really ski here, on real mountains!"

"I'm so glad. I'm sure we'll love it," said Mandy, quite mechanically.

After they hung up, Mandy still didn't feel like sleeping. There was too much to do. She walked into the kitchen to see the pile of dirty dishes left from breakfast and the hurried supper. Suddenly she burst into tears. How could she work in a dirty kitchen? It had to be clean to work in. So she set about washing and scrubbing every last dish and pot, the counter, stove top and refrigerator from top to bottom. Then she decided it was time to clean out the cupboards. Yes, she would start packing the things she didn't need any more. After all, she'd already packed some of the household things, and there was still so much to do. Alan would be so pleased that she was doing so much to help with the move. She decided to call him right now and surprise him with her efficiency, failing to realize that it was now after 2:45 in Toronto, which meant it was pushing midnight in Vancouver.

She dialed, and when he picked up the phone and answered with evident displeasure—there was a three-hour jet lag for him—she merely greeted him with a happy, "Surprise!"

He was surprised all right.

"What the hell are you calling back for, particularly at this hour? Is something wrong?"

There was a slight pause.

"Oh no," said Mandy. "I'm just packing, and I wanted to surprise you."

"Is there something the matter with the kids? Are they all right?"

"Yes, the kids are all right. They look so peaceful huddled together in our bed, honey. I sure miss you."

Something strange was going on. Alan could sense something wrong about the way Mandy sounded. And she didn't seem to respond right away to his questions, but hesitated before answering for several seconds after each question he asked. He tried to pry some information out of her.

"How are you feeling? Are you feeling tired or sick?"

Pause.

"No, I'm fine."

"Have you taken some sort of medication or something? Have you been drinking?"

Five seconds of silence.

"No, I'm fine. I just wanted to surprise you with how efficient I am. You'd be surprised to see how much I've got done. And I miss you, honey. We should be together tonight."

Alan was becoming more apprehensive. Something was very wrong at home and he was 2500 miles away and felt helpless to do anything. Whom could he phone at two in the morning?

"Listen. Try to sleep now; it's late. Don't drink any booze or coffee or anything that will hype you up. Just go to bed, and I'll call you in the morning. You hear?"

"But we went shopping today and we had some stories tonight and I'm the fairy queen and so I really don't need to sleep..."

"Listen!" barked Alan. "I'm going to hang up just now, but don't you go away. Just hang up and wait right there and I'll call you back in just a few minutes. You stay right there, okay?"

"...Okay."

Immediately Alan called Anne Cartwright in Falmouth, catching Ralph angry at being awakened. Once Alan explained the situation, however, Anne, who had taken over the conversation on the other line, was very grateful and they decided quickly to devise a plan.

Alan would call a doctor and also a next-door neighbor, Mrs. Rubin, to check in on Mandy and the children while Anne called Mandy. If Alan was unable to contact Mrs. Rubin and get her to come over and find out the situation, he would call the doctor or— as a last resort—an ambulance. Meanwhile, Anne was to talk to Mandy and see if she could talk her into getting help by herself.

The phone rang in Willowdale. When Mandy heard her mother's voice it was as if the sound were coming through a long tunnel, pulling her out of a dream.

"Mandy, honey, are you okay?" Anne's voice was tense.

There was silence for a few seconds.

"Hi Mom. I'm okay. I'm just packing."

Anne didn't want to alarm Mandy or do anything to make her hang up.

"We're very concerned, dear. Where are the children?"

"Oh, let me get them. They'd be thrilled to death to talk to you. Just a minute."

Anne didn't try to prevent Mandy from waking the children even though it was nearing three in the morning. Somehow it was best to let Mandy bring them to the phone. At least she could find out if they were all right.

Mandy hurried into the master bedroom, the light still on, and woke Stephanie, excited to be sharing her children with their grand-parents. They loved their grandchildren so much, and Mandy knew how they missed not being closer to watch the children's growth.

Mandy had no sense of time or perspective at this point. That such a conversation at this time of night was extraordinary or inappropriate had no meaning for her.

She wanted to give her parents all the time they wanted to talk to the kids, and woke them both. She pulled the covers off them, saying, "Gramma wants to talk with you. Sit up. Hurry." Stephanie was frightened and startled to be so awakened from her deep sleep. The little girl squinted from the bright lights in the bedroom and, totally confused, wondered whether it was early morning or late night. Yes, she wanted to speak to Gramma, but something was wrong. Mommy's smile was almost pasted on her face. And her eyes looked so wide. By now Stephen was also awake, sitting up in bed and yawning.

Sleepily, Stephanie began to chat with her grandparents. Mandy started to think of perhaps driving home right now for a short visit. While Stephanie talked and Stephen slumped on the bed, she went to the closet and took down a suitcase from the shelf.

"Oh, wouldn't it be so nice to be all together," Mandy said to no one in particular. "What a surprise it could be driving home for a quick visit." Stephanie saw the suitcase and began to feel anxious. She interrupted her conversation with Anne to ask, "Mommy, where are you going?" Anne overheard the question. Not having a clue as to what was happening, she became really frightened. "What's happening?" she yelled into the phone. She listened and heard Stephanie crying.

"Don't hang up, Stephanie," Anne pleaded. "Stay on the line. Let me talk to your mother."

Just then the doorbell rang. Erna Rubin, the woman who lived next door to the Marsdens, had often looked after their house or watered the plants if they were gone for a weekend outing or holidays. But she was ill prepared to know how to handle this situation. Alan had only told her that something strange was going on, and could she please check? Standing in the cold with a heavy coat over her nightclothes, she rang the doorbell. She was terrified of what she might find. She heard music coming from the house, and lights were on. Scared half to death she opened the door and called in, "Hello. Is anyone here? Mandy? Are you there?"

She was greatly relieved when Mandy skipped down the stairs very cheerfully. Mandy was so surprised to see Mrs. Rubin.

"Is that you, Mrs. Rubin? Come in. I was just about to make some coffee. Is that really you?"

Mandy was having trouble focusing again. Was this a dream?

"I just got a phone call from Alan. He's worried about you and the children and asked me to come over to see if you're all right. Are you all right? Is there anything wrong with the children?"

"Alan is so sweet," said Mandy. "We're fine, just talking to my folks right now. Come in and make yourself at home. I'm just packing."

Mandy excused herself and went back to the children. Mrs. Rubin walked through to the kitchen and could see that something wasn't quite right. Music blared from the family room and the kitchen—different music from each room. Boxes lay strewn over the floor, half filled with an array of kitchen pots, dishes and utensils. The house was bathed in bright light, and it had the look of five people bustling about. She wandered down the hall to the stairway leading to the bedrooms upstairs just as Mandy called her name. Filled with anxiety, Mrs. Rubin walked upstairs, her hand tightly clutching the rail.

Mandy was sitting on her bed talking on the phone. Both children sat beside her. Stephanie was crying softly. Stephen, his mouth hanging open, stared blankly at Mrs. Rubin as she stood in the doorway, still wearing her heavy coat.

Tears were glistening from Mandy's eyes. Her mother was telling her to trust her, to believe that she was ill and needed to go to the hospital. Mrs. Rubin, looking over at them, saw only three helpless people sitting on the bed. Both children were in tears now that their mother was crying, but also because of their own confusion and discomfort. They were tired and didn't understand what was happening.

Mandy put the phone on her lap for a moment, looked at the children and spoke solemnly: "The fairy queen doesn't live here, but we have to go on a search for our family roots anyway. We're going searching, but first we're going home to see Gramma."

This was too much for the children to understand. Frightened, they simply sat on the bed and cried. Mandy put the phone to her ear again, listened for a few moments and then handed it to Mrs. Rubin. Anne spoke quickly with her. Alan was calling a doctor or an ambulance; probably an ambulance would be arriving soon. She and Ralph would fly up as soon as possible. Mrs. Rubin agreed to watch the children until they arrived. If she could just call Alan back when the ambulance came...

Ambulance! Mandy heard the word from Mrs. Rubin and concluded that she must be really sick. How sad it all was. She wanted so much to surprise everyone with a nice visit. But now it would have to wait. She didn't feel physically tired but was very tired of her head racing. Why were the children crying? It was so sad to see the children upset. She didn't want to hurt anyone, but just wanted everything to be all right. She hugged them both in her arms and resigned herself to whatever came next. Her mission was over. Somehow she had failed, but didn't even know quite how. Everything seemed so confusing.

Mrs. Rubin gave the phone back to Mandy and left the room. Her mother's voice came through the receiver; so comforting, it sounded. It was going to be all right, her mother was saying. Since no one else was available to see her, Mandy was to go to the hospital in the ambulance and they would check her over. Alan would be there soon and so would they. Everything would be all right if she would just go with the ambulance. Mandy seemed to find no problem with that idea.

In a short time an ambulance pulled up in front of the house. No siren blared, no lights flashed. At the door Mrs. Rubin met two attendants in white coats, and the three of them walked upstairs to the bedroom, where Mandy and the children still sat. She didn't like the way they looked at her as everyone walked downstairs. She didn't trust them somehow. At the bottom of the stairs Mrs. Rubin was saying, "Now don't you worry about the children. They'll be fine with me for the time being..."

Something about that bothered Mandy. Suddenly she remembered her unicorn and without a word dashed upstairs to get it. Passing by the children's rooms she suddenly realized that they too must go to the hospital, to be with her. She couldn't have them be frightened.

She had to get some things for the children but couldn't keep the men waiting, so she had to hurry.

By now, however, the ambulance attendants were in pursuit up the stairs after their patient. As they met Mandy in the hallway, their faces appeared to grow huge before her. Mandy squinted her eyes, trying to focus on them. She didn't really understand what was happening but only recognized that she had to protect herself and the children from harm. Seeing the attendants looming before her, she backed up into Stephen's room, unicorn in hand, and tried to shut the door. The two men saw only a woman with a wild look in her eye, and they lunged for the door, preventing her from closing it. Hearing the noise and confusion, Stephanie and Stephen started to cry, and Mrs. Rubin put her arms around them both to comfort them and to keep them from what was happening.

The next few minutes were exceptionally painful for everyone. The two men, completely distrustful of people suffering from mental disorders, had been trained to use their strength to overcome reluctant or dangerous patients. Quickly, easily, they grabbed Mandy, pinning her arms behind her, and pushed her roughly before them as they went downstairs. She became terribly frightened with the crushing feeling of being restrained.

"Please stop!" she cried in pain. "You're hurting me. Please let me go. I need my babies. Please let them come."

Other lights came on in nearby houses. But Mandy noticed none of it, nor did she hear what Mrs. Rubin was saying as one of the attendants pushed Mandy into the back of the ambulance and pulled the door closed behind him. Lights flashing, the ambulance left a cloud of acrid fumes in the street as it raced off into the night.

Mandy's mind and body were completely lost in a flood of chemical reactions within her. She vaguely noticed lights pass by above her and heard the faint but sharp sounds of a radio as she lay strapped to the bed. She could do nothing but melt; it didn't seem to matter any more. She'd lost; she seemed to let go and sank into the bed, and it felt good. It didn't even matter that she now lay in a puddle of warm urine. It didn't matter at all any more.

Chapter Fifteen

The next few hours were only a blur of movements for Mandy. She knew she was in a hospital because of all the white uniforms and the sterile, antiseptic smell. The lights on the ceiling glared too brightly, she thought as she lay on the gurney for what seemed a long time. She could hear voices talking, some speaking to her, asking questions: What was her name? Did she have children? What were their names? It was difficult to concentrate. What was real and what wasn't? She kept thinking she must be in a dream, and her head felt so heavy when she tried to lift herself. She lay quietly, her eyes half open—they seemed unable to stay open for more than a moment at a time.

People wouldn't leave her alone. They kept asking questions and moving her around from one place to another. How much time had passed she didn't know. It didn't seem to matter. She tried to focus on people's faces. Some appeared to be larger than normal. The voices also seemed amplified; they boomed as if spoken through a tunnel or huge megaphone. She strained as if to look for someone in particular. She felt definitely that she was on remote control, that someone else was operating her movements. Every muscle was strained and tense, trying to receive some clue through her senses, just as an animal would in the wild.

Where was her family? She must find them. But how could she do that until they let her go? It was strange, disquieting, to feel so helpless. Something within her managed to keep her inwardly calm, and a still, small feeling of peace began to spread and drift up from her deepest being, to let her feel somehow safe, even if she wasn't terribly aware of events taking place around her. She was to do as she was told, so she could relax even though the search for family roots kept coming back into her mind.

Mandy was finally allowed to sleep, and when she woke and

looked around, she found herself alone, wearing a white frock and lying on a bed, in a single room with nothing in it but her bed, a chair and a small night table. She sat up very groggily and noticed a good-sized paper bag sitting beside the bed. In it she found a few familiar belongings—her clothes, all neatly folded, her shoes and her stuffed unicorn.

She tried to focus on where she was, what she was doing here, but her mind was a sea of confused thoughts. She had to fight to force her thoughts to stay in order. Even trying to stand was an effort. Every movement she made seemed to be in slow motion. The door to the corridor was open, and with effort she slowly made her way out into the hall and stood in front of the doorway. Where was she? A nurse appeared suddenly in the hallway carrying a tray; as she walked past—was she smiling?—she greeted Mandy with a face that didn't want to stay in focus.

"Don't go too far, Mrs. Marsden," the nurse said. "Doctor Bertinelli wants to see you."

That statement didn't mean much to Mandy—she didn't know any doctor named Bertinelli. The nurse must have been talking to someone else. Mandy put her hands up against the door frame and squinted her eyes, concentrating, trying desperately to find something or someone to relate with. Her senses were again leading her. She walked toward the end of the hall. Ahead of her was a large sitting area—couches, TV, a bookcase full of assorted reading material. Men and women sat in easy chairs watching TV or in stiff-backed wooden chairs hunched over game tables, and several people simply stood still, one or two looking out the windows and several others just staring into space. Except for the sound of the television set, there was surprisingly little noise from the fifteen or so people assembled in the room. Directly to Mandy's left was a nursing station, where two nurses sat flipping through charts behind a low counter and a desk.

Mandy noticed an old woman sitting in a chair facing a window, just rocking back and forth. Everyone else seemed only a blur. The phone rang softly every few minutes, and two announcements came in quick succession over the public address speaker that hung on the wall.

Mandy realized where she was. But why, she wondered. A

magazine on the table caught her eye. It seemed to be beckoning her. On the cover the words "You Are The One" leaped out at her. Yes, she believed she was, and now her thoughts began to race once again, tumbling over each other. She had a special mission. She must find her children, re-establish family roots and then she could save the world from hurting any more. First, however, she had to get out of here. But wait. She picked up another book to see if it too held a message, just as a nurse took her arm and said, "The doctor would like to see you now."

The nurse ushered Mandy back to her room. Doctor Bertinelli sat in the chair and smiled as Mandy entered the room with the nurse. He was a large, round man, about fifty, with a balding head and bushy grey hair that pushed out and curled on the sides of his head. When he spoke he had a rich, resonant voice that sounded kind to Mandy's ears.

"Hello, Amanda," he said, rising with outstretched hand from the chair. "I'm Doctor Bertinelli. I'm going to be your doctor for a little while."

"Hello," Mandy replied, and took his hand hesitantly. "Please call me Mandy."

"Do you know what's happened to you in the last little while, Mandy?" he asked bluntly. "Do you know why you're here?"

Mandy felt very tired. She couldn't remember everything, but she did feel sad as she thought about the last time she saw Stephanie and Stephen. They were huddled together in tears in the front hallway as she was taken away.

"I think I'm here to get well." Her mother had told her that, so she knew.

"But can I please go now? I have work to do, and I really should be home."

"Well, Mandy, I'm afraid you'll have to stay here for a little while, at least until we can fully assess what went wrong. Something is agitating you, and we have to make some corrections concerning that. So we want to try some medication for a little while to calm you down a bit, since you've been very agitated."

When he mentioned medication Mandy became frightened and resolved to leave immediately. After all, she really felt fine, except for being so tired.

"I'll pop in from time to time to see how you're doing, Mandy. In the meantime, make yourself at home. Feel free to go down to the lounge and relax. There's nothing to worry about while you're here. If you need anything, just ask one of the nurses." He paused and smiled.

"Here, Mandy. Drink this. It'll make you feel relaxed. It's been a long day."

She sat on the edge of the bed and took the paper cup and drank the contents. Doctor Bertinelli smiled again and left the room with the nurse.

Mandy's eyes again became difficult to keep open. Not long after the doctor left she was back in bed, asleep for what seemed an eternity. She came to with the sound of a voice calling her name.

"Mandy, wake up. It's time to take your pills. The doctor wants to start you on these. They should make you less drowsy."

Mandy sat up and tried to focus. The room was a blur, and all she could see was a hand with a little cup with two pink and green capsules posed right in front of her face. Her hand shook slightly as she reached for the pills. The nurse handed her another small cup full of water. Mandy drank them down, trusting that she would be fine.

The bed felt uncomfortable at the moment and she decided to get up and walk for a while. The corridor was filled with people now—nurses and patients wandering about. She walked unsteadily down to the lounge and looked around. An old man sat asleep in a chair right beside the entrance. The clock on the wall read 5:15, so it had to be close to supper time. Few of the people there even moved, and no one seemed interested in talking.

Mandy was feeling very alone right now. She had to talk to someone, to someone she knew. Yes, she would call home. She walked over to the nurse's station and asked, smiling, "Is there a phone here?"

Without looking up from her papers the nurse pointed with her pen to the corridor to her right. "It's on the wall."

Standing before the phone she remembered she didn't have any change—and besides, whom could she talk to? A feeling of growing panic started creeping up her spine and into her head. She struggled again with her thoughts, with what she should be remembering. What was her home phone number? Oh, she wanted so much to see the children right now. They were her whole life. What were they going to do without her? Who was taking care of them now? She couldn't remember. And what about Alan? Why wasn't he here? Couldn't he take me home? Tears started down her cheeks as she wandered once more into the lounge and past the couch, defeated. Where could she go? She looked around the room for someone, anyone to identify with. A young girl in a pink bathrobe and fluffy slippers approached her. Mandy tried to smile, but the girl just passed without even seeming to notice her. Two middle-aged women sat smoking cigarettes and shaking their heads in quiet conversation over on the other side of the room. The TV station was tuned to the news broadcast, and a few people stared blankly into the screen.

A nurse called from the station area that the trays for supper were up, and suddenly, as if they were robots, each of the patients began clearing the lounge. They walked down the hall to the cafeteria, with Mandy in tow, hoping someone would tell her where she was going.

She had little appetite but thought that dinner would pass the time. Besides, there might be someone to talk with. So she followed the others and reached for a tray. On the plate was a nondescript slice of meat with gravy, two boiled potatoes and some sliced carrots that stared at her, a carton of milk and a small container of brown pudding. Just as she turned to carry it over to the tables, a woman reached in front of her and grabbed the tray. "Hey," she screamed, "what do you think you're doing? That's mine."

She grabbed the tray from Mandy and shot her an ugly, threatening look as she turned and, in a huff, headed for a table. Two male attendants came over quickly to see what was the matter.

"I'm sorry," Mandy said. "I didn't know the tray belonged to anyone."

Mandy hadn't noticed the little name tag tucked under the milk in the corner of the tray. One of the attendants was courteous enough to take a few moments to explain the rules and procedures of the cafeteria, after which he sent her off to look for her own tray. It wasn't there. She couldn't find one with her name and had to go to the nurse's station again. The nurse assured her she would call down to have a tray sent up. By this time Mandy was feeling very uncomfortable. No one liked her, it seemed, and she wanted to go home. Besides, she was feeling that same pumping of energy again, that rush of adrenaline.

She had to move around. The walls seemed to be closing in. She paced the halls looking for some friendly eyes or some familiar landmark. She felt trapped and needed to be free to search for her roots. She was getting hot now. She didn't like this hospital gown and silly robe they gave her. Where were her own things? That's what she wanted to wear. She went back to her room and, standing in the middle of the floor, decided she had to use the bathroom. Having finished, she stood looking down over the toilet, watching the flushed water swirl around, slowly, it seemed, then in a wider and stronger flow, becoming larger and louder. Somehow the water called to her. She reached down and put her hand into the swirling water just as a nurse came into the room bringing her a dinner tray and the next pills. Horrified at what she saw, the nurse quickly sprang into the bathroom and pulled Mandy's hand out of the water and sat her down on the edge of the bed. "You don't want to do that," she said. "Are you feeling all right?"

"Yes."

"Here, take these and we'll have to check with the doctor." Mandy suddenly felt very ashamed of what she had done. She realized where her hand had been. Over and over the thought went through her mind, Oh dear God, what's happening to me? But no words came out.

"I'll be back in a few minutes," said the nurse. "I think we'd like to have you sit in the lounge for a while. So once you have your supper you can come down. Do you feel like going to the cafeteria?"

"Oh yes, I'm fine now."

She would eat and then go to the lounge as she was told. But as the nurse turned and left, Mandy saw the white of her dress consume her and she felt uncomfortable. The blanket of white filled her view until she closed her eyes and opened them again. The nurse was gone. Mandy spotted the unicorn beside the bag and decided it needed to be with her. Taking the unicorn in her arms, she felt that from somewhere inside her body a message was being conveyed: she would be all right.

But she was so hot, so damp in this stiff frock. If only she could have her own things. Slowly, methodically she took off her robe and undid the nighty and let it slip to the floor. Perhaps she would just go to the front desk first and ask if she could have her own nighty. As if in a dream she started walking, stark naked, out of her room. It took only a few steps into the corridor before someone noticed her. She could see the disgust and the sternness on the faces coming toward her, so she smiled to ease their concern. The next thing she knew there were four people struggling to hold her down. Why were they doing this? What had she done? In self-defense she fought them as best she could, but they had her pinned to the floor and couldn't move at all. She felt encased in the white of their uniforms, stifled, as if she were smothering, and in panic she tried to scream, but nothing came out. One of the attendants reached across and injected her in the rump with a needle of something that instantly made her lose her grip. Her strength seemed to melt away, and her vision became clouded. The nurses and attendants, seeming blurred, moved as if in slow motion toward the door and out into the corridor. The door closed.

Please no, thought Mandy. I don't want to be alone. Oh no, please don't shut the door. She slid off the bed and moved toward the door in the same slow motion, it seemed, and as if from a tunnel she heard the click of a lock being secured from the outside.

She could see only a narrow line of light from above and below the door, but looking into it Mandy saw nothing, just emptiness. Huddling against the door, she brought her arms to herself and cried herself to sleep.

When she woke up the room was still dark and she found herself in bed. A few minutes later a nurse entered and asked how she felt. Dutifully, she tried to concentrate on how she felt, but even that was difficult. She seemed dizzy and a little sore on her left side. Her eyes had trouble staying open; she desperately tried to keep the lids from drooping. Maybe if she sat up her eyes would stay open. She pushed herself into a sitting position. But then her head seemed heavy and strained to one side, as if to be listening for something, some key to feeling comfortable or something familiar. She didn't like the coolness of the sheets against her leg. "Can I get up?" she asked.

Mandy vaguely remembered what had happened, why they

had drugged her, but was embarrassed to ask the nurse anything about it. "Yes, you can," the nurse replied. There was no mention of Mandy's nakedness nor that she'd had to be restrained. Mandy didn't even know how long she'd been asleep. In effect, she was left to wonder if the whole thing had taken place only in her imagination. It might have, because she knew something about her wasn't working properly—her movements seemed to be very slow and she always felt so sleepy.

It was two more days of observation before Mandy heard anything from her family. Anne Cartwright had flown up to relieve Mrs. Rubin of responsibility for the children. Alan was flying back from Vancouver. His transfer was being reassessed, contingent on what the doctors might decide when they met tomorrow. Needless to say, the whole family was stunned, in a state of shock and confusion over the breakdown.

Everyone, that is, except Mandy. She was off in her own world trying to decipher her real feelings, to separate them from delusions and misguided thought patterns. It was strange, but during the whole experience she felt as if she were being guided. Very strongly she sensed God's love and protection, and often she felt a gentle peace and trust in spite of her general discomfort in the hospital. She would sit and stare dreamily into space with a sad smile on her face, wondering, in her drug-altered world, what was real and what was fantasy.

True to form, Mandy tried always to please the hospital workers, who had such heavy responsibility for their charges. She was willing to submit to anything they had in store, for they knew best. And she tried to become friends with them, but the hospital was ultimately a cold, unfriendly environment where the workers seldom had time to sit and chat, and most of the patients couldn't carry on a reasonable conversation. Mandy wanted so much to talk to someone, but everyone seemed always to be scurrying about. No nurse had time to stop and chat unless she was passing out medication—and even then it was as if the short "conversation" were only a ruse to get patients to take their pills. Sometimes she got the feeling that they were staring at her, even talking or laughing about her as she passed the nurse's station. If only she could get out of here and be home with her family.

Mandy was returning from the lounge with a book in her hand when she saw her mother walking down the hall with Alan and Doctor Bertinelli. She squinted, thinking this must be a dream. Alan didn't look happy, she could tell. He tried to smile as he approached, but Mandy's senses had become very sharp and she could almost read the unsettled thoughts behind his countenance.

Then, as Alan peered closely at Mandy she suddenly felt extremely self-conscious. She hadn't seen herself in a mirror for days. Her hands went up to her hair, trying to smooth it down. I must look a mess, she thought. This afternoon I'm going to just have to fix myself up.

Alan came close and gave her a quick, stiff hug and a kiss on the cheek. Mandy sensed the coolness. "How are you?" he asked, trying to be genuine.

She looked into his eyes and felt tears filling her own and whispered, "I'm sorry for bringing you back. I'm sorry for always causing everyone so much trouble. I don't know what's wrong with me."

Anne tried to comfort Mandy, and when she realized her mother was also there, she reached for her and in the comfort of her mother's arms she finally let go of her emotions. Alan and the doctor separated from mother and daughter, and paced slowly down the hall engrossed in close conversation. After a few moments Anne gently turned Mandy, and together they walked toward her room. With Alan standing near the window and Anne seated with her arm around Mandy's waist on the bed, Doctor Bertinelli began to explain what was wrong with Mandy—he called it a manic-depressive, affective disorder. The words meant nothing to her. Alan, somewhat removed from everyone else, leaned against the window sill and stared outside. After explaining the symptoms of Mandy's disorder, the doctor said that they would like to keep Mandy in the hospital for observation and to see if they could stabilize her apparent mania with a combination of lithium and an anti-depressant medicine with a long name that didn't register in Mandy's mind.

It was all too confusing. All she heard was that they wanted to keep her in the hospital. How could she do that? The children needed her, and they were in the middle of moving. She started to feel a rush of heat coming to her face, and her heart seemed to be picking up speed. She became agitated.

Anne, conscious of a physical change in Mandy, tried to soothe her nervousness.

"That's all right, dear," she reassured her daughter, "everything will still be fine. You can be with the children in a few weeks. We'll take care of them. Don't you worry."

Oh my God, Mandy thought, I don't want to be here a few weeks.

Doctor Bertinelli looked at Alan and said, "Under the circumstances, perhaps you'd better discuss the situation regarding the relocation you'd planned."

Alan walked to the bed and sat down beside Mandy, taking her hand. "My transfer's been postponed," he said. "The people at the firm think this is a serious problem for us, and they just think that a move right now might be very dangerous for you, especially since nobody's really sure how serious your illness is."

Mandy dropped her eyes to her lap and clenched her hands, knowing what was to come.

"It's just going to take more time, and you have to get the right medication before we do anything."

Mandy knew everyone had been talking about her—the "people at the firm," the doctors and nurses, even Alan. And they had made decisions without asking her. She felt so crippled, so helpless, so weak. Why hadn't they asked her? She suddenly found the energy to defend herself. After all, she didn't want to have another failure on her conscience.

"I'll be all right in a few days. I know I'm okay."

She began to feel panic. Tears of hopelessness welled up within her.

"Can't we still go, Alan? I want you to have your dream. I won't spoil things again, I promise. Please!"

The feelings began to overtake her. Her words were lost in helpless sobs of frustration.

"I think you'd better rest now," Alan said.

"We'll discuss this later," said the doctor with a nod of

agreement toward Alan.

Anne, of course, couldn't help but notice Alan's callousness toward Mandy. From everything he said and did, it seemed that he was concerned only with himself, with getting out of the hospital as soon as he possibly could. Where was his compassion for his wife? Anne wanted so much for her daughter to be happy, and in the depths of her heart wished for a good, happy life together for Alan and Mandy and the children. But she couldn't help feeling resentful toward her son-in-law's behavior, and it showed. Anne stared knives through him, but her anger was muted by her feelings for her daughter, and she realized that the whole family was under terrible strain right now. She couldn't believe that her daughter, lying there so helpless and hurt, had been labeled a manic-depressive mental patient. She saw only a very loving and fragile girl full of sensitivity and caring. But simply pointing that out to the doctor—or Alan—wouldn't help. She leaned down to kiss Mandy goodbye.

"I'll be back tomorrow," she said with a smile. "Get some rest, dear."

She hugged her daughter, shot Alan a cold look and left the room, the two men behind her.

Mandy, whose emotional senses had somehow become acutely sharpened as a sort of byproduct of her disease, almost physically experienced the pain her family was going through. She felt so responsible and guilty for causing such turmoil, for upsetting their lives so completely. She was so horrible. Self-deprecating thoughts filled her mind, worked on her as she lay on her bed. Eventually she drifted into fitful sleep.

When she came to, she felt as if her mind were fuzzy, not so much that her thoughts were unclear, but there seemed to be layers of fuzz just where her brain should be. Suddenly she realized that a nice hot shower just might clear her head of this fuzz. Taking her towel from the drawer, she tied her robe, put on slippers and walked out of her room and down the hall to the shower room. On entering, she felt vaguely that she wasn't alone. She looked around but saw no one. Shrugging off the feeling, she slipped off her robe and slippers and walked over to the shower stall. The floor was cool on her bare feet as she turned on the water in the shower. She felt warm and peaceful.

And as the hot water rushed over her, she began to feel that this had all been a terrible dream. She was well and whole; the water was purifying and healing her, washing away every bad thought. As she moved her hands over her skin, made incredibly smooth by the soap, and rubbed her fingers through her hair, she suddenly felt stronger and more in control than she had ever been. Yes, this was all a bad dream. When she emerged from the shower everyone would recognize their mistake. They would see who she really was. She was the creature that God had sent to save this world from any more hurt.

Mandy became tremendously excited at what she was feeling. A great joy and exhilaration consumed her as she let the water spray its knowledge to every pore of her skin. She felt magnificent, superhuman, full of such love and compassion that she found herself beginning to cry, but the tears were of overwhelming happiness because now all the pain would be gone.

As she shut off the shower and reached for the towel, she became more excited about what she was going to see in the mirror. Had God changed her looks? Would there be a noticeable difference? How would God allow everyone to know that she was The Chosen One? Was she to be the Messiah? Was she to become a man? Nervously she looked down at her naked body to see if she was still all there. This isn't good enough, she thought—where's the mirror? As she stepped hesitantly from the shower stalls to look into the full-length mirror that faced her now, she was puzzled. There she saw herself naked, just another rather small and vulnerable human being. She hadn't been transformed at all! She was still Mandy. Confused, she started to become disoriented.

What was God's plan for her? What was happening? She struggled against the fuzz and concentrated, trying to focus on the eyes that seemed to beckon her from the mirror. The fuzziness began to clear.

Next she noticed her hair. It had been recently cut and permed, and now it was disheveled from the shower, so Mandy quickly roughed it up with the towel. Her eyes ran down the line of her body. Somehow it was still in very good shape. She liked what she saw. Her eyes glanced down from her still firm breasts to her rib cage and on to her rounded belly, with its signs of childbirth and the scar just above the pubic bone that marked the second caesarean.

Mandy began to love the person she saw. She remembered that God loved her and was taking care of her. If only she could remember to place her trust in Him, everything would be all right... A smile came to her face as she gave herself another sidewards glance. Grabbing the towel, she dried off energetically and again felt that same peace and calm that meant she was going to make it. She would survive this and more. She felt strong and sure.

A feeling of contentment, a softness toward herself and the world, remained with Mandy—that is, until Alan came to visit again that night.

He walked into her room unannounced and started to walk over to the bed where she sat reading. At the sound Mandy looked up and immediately was delighted to see him, and the yellow roses he was bringing her. But something about his presence wasn't right. Something in his eyes. He smiled and looked just as he always did—handsomely masculine and well-dressed in his sweater and slacks. Behind the smile, however, Mandy sensed a great sadness, an anger, almost a fury at the way his plans had been thwarted. And clearly, she was the cause. Instantly she was afraid to be near him, afraid of hurting him again in some way. She forced herself to smile back at him.

"Oh Alan, they're just gorgeous!" she exclaimed. "I'll have to put them in some water right away. You're such a sweetheart."

"Well, I just thought they'd cheer up the room a bit."

He sat next to her on the bed.

"How are you tonight?" he asked.

"Oh, I'm okay, I guess. It's good to see you. How are the kids?"

"They're home watching TV. Your mom's always got her eye on them, so there's never any problem with what they're doing. She sees to that."

"I wish I could see them. I miss them so much... How are you doing?"

"Well, things could be better, I suppose," he said, getting up and walking over to the window. He peered into the darkness.

"I've decided it's best to stay in Toronto, what with your

illness and everything. Oh, everything will come together all right. It just can't be helped; it's just one of those things that happen."

He turned to look at her—almost as if to somehow challenge her, Mandy thought—but she dared not say anything for fear of saying something wrong and hurting him. He was honestly trying to care about her feelings, to lessen the gravity of the great loss to his career plans.

"Now we just want you to get well, so stay here as long as it takes," he added.

Mandy detected a coolness in his words and his bearing. Try as he might, he was having difficulty hiding his real feelings of resentment toward her. In turn, she felt as much frustration as he. She wanted to go home! She felt like such a weakling, not to be able to control her head better. But she couldn't cry in front of him, not tonight. Besides, she didn't really feel as if she could cry. The lithium, or whatever it was they were always giving her, seemed to numb parts of her mind. She was attentive and some of her inner senses were very sharp and perceptive, but in other ways she wasn't quite all there—and then the slow motion and dullness would take over.

Alan's words jarred her mind back from its wandering.

"Well, I shouldn't stay because you ought to have your rest," he said.

"Yes, I guess I'm pretty tired tonight. And you shouldn't have to be out anyway."

He leaned over and kissed her on the cheek, and as he walked toward the door, said, "I'll call tomorrow. Get a good night's sleep."

"You too. Drive carefully. I love you, Alan."

The door closed, and tears trickled down her cheeks.

"God, am I really crazy? If I am, please just let me die."

The next week seemed to drag on endlessly for Mandy. She didn't really know when one day ended and one began except for the food that showed up on her tray at each meal. She didn't seem to have energy to do any more than walk the halls or sit alone in the lounge, perhaps to read a magazine. At least this was a diversion from staring at the walls or the ceiling in her room, wondering what had happened to her.

Other thoughts and questions often recurred. Why did she

keep having those feelings of being someone special? Such thoughts were alien to her; in real life—she made a wry smile at the notion—she wanted only to be a good wife and mother. Why did faces loom toward her at times, fading in and out? And words become slowed as people spoke? Then there was the slow motion that she often thought she saw. Am I simply nuts or is something else causing some of this, she wondered? Could the pills have anything to do with her strange perceptions? Why did she have to keep taking those damned pills? They made her mouth so dry all the time. Someone was at least aware of the thirst, because there was always lots to drink in the cafeteria. Mandy couldn't help but notice how many people always added piles of sugar to their coffee. Maybe the pills did that too, but then why not to her? She didn't use any sugar at all. Sometimes the smell of stale cigarette smoke was so strong in the TV room that she couldn't bear to be in the room. If only she could get away from here and the damned medicine.

One morning Mandy awoke slowly, and with conscious effort moved to get out of bed. Sitting on the edge, she noticed a tightness in the joints, a slight ache in her bones. I must be getting old, she concluded. Not enough exercise. Then, as she dropped her nighty and reached for her robe so she could go to the shower room, she noticed a rash on her hands and ankles. Moving her hands to her face, she felt her skin. Nothing different. But then she noticed a roughness on her neck. Concerned, she went to the shower room and the mirror to examine herself more closely. Her face and eyelids looked puffy, and a patch of rash was on the left side, above the hip.

The morning nurse briefly examined the puffiness on Mandy's face and eyes and the skin rash. "I don't think it's much to worry about," she offered. "We'll keep our eye on it, but it'll probably be gone by this evening."

By afternoon, however, when the nurse entered with the next dose of medication, the swelling had become so pronounced that she immediately sent for Doctor Bertinelli, who, it happened, wasn't anywhere to be found.

For the afternoon Mandy stayed in her room, and an attendant brought in her dinner tray and several magazines. Shortly after seven o'clock, Alan appeared at the door.

"Holy shit," he blurted. "What's wrong? Are you all right? What happened?"

Mandy, covered in rash, seriously swollen, and sore in her joints, lay in bed terribly embarrassed by her appearance. The sight of Alan at the door immediately brought her recollection of how she'd looked after the earlier kidney failure, her face and knees all puffed up like basketballs. She was enormously self-conscious about how terrible she must look and just knew her looks would drive Alan away.

"I don't know what's happened," she said. "They sent for Doctor Bertinelli, but he hasn't shown up yet. No one seems to know where he is."

"What the hell kind of place is this, anyway?" Alan snorted in disgust. "Isn't there another doctor around here? What the fuck is going on?"

Afraid that he would create a scene, Mandy tried to divert his attention. "Oh Alan, it's okay," she said. "They know what's going on, and he'll be here after a while. They're watching out for me. How are the kids?"

Alan fumed as he stared alternately at Mandy and out the window. "They're okay, but your mother babies them too much. She spends all her time over them, playing with them, entertaining them, reading them fifty stories a day." He threw his hands into the air. "She's spoiling them rotten!"

He was angry and at the moment cared little about what he said.

Mandy, surprised at herself, went on the defensive for her children. "What do you want them to do, get a job? After all, they're only kids, and remember, you didn't have much of a childhood, so how would you know what was right? How many fairy tales can you remember?"

Alan, still hot, glared at his wife's swollen features and suddenly realized she was quite seriously ill. Then he knew that if he said any more, he'd say things he'd later regret. This wasn't the time to blow up. He tried to control himself.

"I don't want to be interrogated, especially tonight," he said. "I've got a big presentation to give in the morning, and it's getting late, so I'd better be going." As he leaned down dutifully to kiss Mandy, she could see him shut his eyes almost in revulsion, and she became self-conscious and unsure of how he felt about his sickly wife. She drew back from him in disgust of herself, more than anything.

"Goodnight, Alan," she said, dropping her eyes. "Hope it goes well tomorrow." She picked up a magazine and mindlessly flipped the pages. "If you're too tired, don't bother coming up tomorrow night. I'll be okay."

"Well, you call me tomorrow and let me know how you're doing. Make sure you talk to the doctor about your rash and stuff first thing tomorrow," he commanded briskly as he turned and disappeared through the doorway.

Mandy sighed deeply. When she knew he was gone, she slapped the magazine down on her lap and cried out, "Am I ever going to be myself again? Oh, I absolutely hate this! Oh God, please help me."

She lay awake most of the night, at the edge of being pulled down into a sea of doubt and fear.

By the time Doctor Bertinelli came on his rounds the next morning, the rash had become red and rough, and the swelling had extended to Mandy's hands and feet. She felt sore all over.

The big man held his clipboard at the side of Mandy's bed and frowned down at her. "You don't look as if you're up to a very exciting day today, do you? Well, we know what the problem is, and it won't be long before this is all cleared up."

He turned to the nurse, and in a voice that Mandy could hear clearly, said, "Well, it's obvious she has to be taken off the lithium immediately, nurse."

Then he quickly mumbled the long name of another drug, turned and walked from the room. The nurse smiled at her and also left. Mandy felt like a piece of furniture. He hadn't even asked how she was feeling! They had looked at her like a specimen under glass, as if she had no eyes or ears or feelings.

By evening, however, the swelling had gone down a great deal, which gave Mandy's sagging spirits a boost. Her mother's arrival brightened her considerably, and they went out to the lounge and talked for almost two hours.

"I want to hear all about what's happening at home," Mandy

pressed.

"Well, let's see. Where shall I start?" Anne asked. As she began to bring Mandy up to date on the latest events at home, Mandy listened hungrily. If only she could be there instead of this terribly depressing place. Wistfully she looked at her mother as she spoke; she looked tired, Mandy thought. I'm sorry she has to work so hard with two such active kids. It must be hard even to adjust from doing things at home in Falmouth to our house here. But Stephanie was growing up fast; she'd soon be five and should be thrilled to help Gramma around the house...

"Oh, I want so much to go home," Mandy blurted, interrupting her mother.

"Well, dear, it won't be long now," Anne said. "We just have to wait till they stabilize your medication, especially since you're allergic to lithium."

Anne was concerned about the allergy and how her daughter might be able to cope now with alternative drugs, but said nothing for fear of upsetting her.

In turn, Mandy noticed her mother's apprehension and also kept quiet. She turned her attention to the other patients in the lounge, some of whom she'd gotten to know somewhat. Speaking in whispers so as not to offend anyone, she gestured to an astonishingly thin girl in her twenties, whom she liked particularly, over by the water fountain.

"She's got something called anorexia, Mom. What's that?" Mandy whispered.

In a low voice her mother tried to explain. "Well, I haven't worked in the hospital for some time now, but I believe it's got something to do with not wanting to eat, because she thinks she's fat even if she's skinny as a rail. So she has to keep dieting, she believes. People can die from complications, I've heard."

Mandy then pointed out an older woman sitting in front of the nurse's station. With tremendous effort she had just walked along the corridor, with the help of a cane, and into the lounge, falling into the closest empty chair. She looked as if she weighed four hundred pounds. Anne was taken aback by the woman's size and the way she gasped for lack of oxygen.

Mandy explained something of her story. The woman had been ill for many years and had become depressed. A physician had given her a drug for her depression but something went wrong with her hormones and she started gaining weight rapidly. She'd tried to kill herself once by jumping in front of a subway car, but apparently her size saved her. She was unconscious in the hospital for about three months and continued to gain more weight because they were still giving her drugs. When she finally came to, she hated herself for not dying because she felt useless to anyone; she was fat, ugly and sick besides. And today she was in the hospital because she was becoming allergic to her drug.

"That's enough, dear," Anne said, shaking her head. "I can't listen to this any more. It's too tragic. Besides, I have to get home for the children now."

They walked back to Mandy's room. It was agony for Anne to leave her daughter like this, in this place, especially since she knew so much about Mandy's illness. But she tried desperately not to let her daughter sense anything but hope and optimism in her words as she kissed her goodnight and left.

Mandy felt especially good this evening; she wanted to stay in the lounge and talk to anyone who would listen. After several frustrating, abortive attempts at conversation she settled for watching TV with two young men who weren't interested in any programs. At midnight a nurse came in to shut it off. The fat lady lay fast asleep, her vast bulk sprawled on the corner couch. Another older woman sat alone on a straight-backed wooden chair, staring out a window into the darkness and mumbling to herself. All the other patients had gone to bed.

Back in her room Mandy still felt terribly restless. She undressed for bed, put on her nighty, picked up a pile of magazines on her desk and plopped down onto the bed. Propping her pillow behind her head she began to read through the magazines, carefully scrutinizing every page. After quite some time she was startled by her door suddenly opening. It was one of the nurses.

"What in the world are you still up for?" she asked. Mandy smiled at her with bright, almost glassy eyes.

"I'm just reading. I'm not too sleepy yet."

"Well, little Miss Muffet, maybe you should have a sleeping pill," said the nurse as she checked her clipboard to see what medication Mandy was on.

"I see you had your medication at eleven, so you should be okay till seven. Listen you," she said, pointing a stern finger at Mandy, "that's only three hours away. Try to get some sleep, but you'd have better luck if you turned off the light."

Clipboard under her arm, the nurse turned and went back into the corridor, closing the door.

Mandy breathed a great sigh of relief. She couldn't have told the nurse, but as she entered the room Mandy saw her face suddenly grow larger and its features become cloudy, and her words began to sound slurred. This had happened before, Mandy remembered, but she was afraid to say anything now because she didn't want to be locked up again.

Now that the nurse had gone she could get back to her search. There must be more clues. She was convinced that God was speaking to her now through the magazine. Some words seemed to be highlighted; they almost jumped out at her as if they contained secret, special messages. She was so happy. There was no question that she was truly special, and she knew that if she just kept looking, the evidence would make itself unquestionably plain. Thoughts raced and impulses darted randomly between her eyes and the words on the pages. Every picture held a secret meaning. Mandy was so pleased to have this private talent all to herself. She was really loved now. And she could change this hurtful world. Oh, she was so proud of herself now, for being able to pick up these hidden, extrasensory messages.

She smiled at everyone as she passed the early morning risers on her way to the shower. She loved the purifying ceremony that went on there. The hot needles of clean water purged her of every frailty, every sadness, stinging them out of her and whirling them down into the sewer where they belonged. She scrubbed herself dry with the rough towel, to make sure every last bit of trouble was gone.

After dressing, she passed the nurse's station and walked into the lounge to see if anyone wanted some company. Perhaps she could share her newly discovered good fortune with someone. No one was interested even in talking, but Mandy's enthusiasm and high spirits couldn't be shattered this morning. It was beautiful and clear outside, and it was going to be a good day, a marvelous day. The plants that sat on the window ledge seemed almost to become animated as she looked at them. The shaggy Boston fern seemed to grow greener right before her eyes. She couldn't believe how free and comfortable she felt! It was so good to be so healthy, so vibrant, so alive—with two beautiful, healthy children.

The wonderful aroma of fresh coffee wafted along the corridor. Mandy turned to head down toward the cafeteria and noticed the same gray-haired woman who last evening was in the TV room and mumbling to herself. She was sitting on a bench in the hall and staring off into space, a cigarette sticking out of her mouth. A long ash drooped from the end, and a circle of smoke hung over her head. How unhealthy that is, Mandy thought. She liked this woman and didn't want her to die from smoking, so she decided to do something to help her. She suddenly spied the water jug sitting on the counter at the nurse's station. Calmly, without a word, she walked over and picked it up. The nurse looked up from her newspaper with a lazy glance. Mandy smiled back, then she walked deliberately over to the woman, lifted the jug over her head and poured out the entire contents, drenching the woman and, of course, extinguishing the cigarette. Horrified, the woman tried to duck the cold water, throwing her arms upward, then she jumped up shrieking her indignation at the top of her lungs in a loud chorus of profanities.

Immediately on alert, the two nurses nearby sprang into action. From behind the desk at the nursing station they hurried briskly down the corridor and took hold of Mandy, grabbing the water jug from her hand. Quickly they ushered her down the corridor and into her room. Mandy saw disgust on their faces and recognized, with a great rush of sadness, that she had alienated herself again.

"I promise I'll be good," she wailed, starting to cry. "Please don't think I'm bad."

She was so mixed up now. All she was trying to do was to help that woman. Wasn't that clear to them? In frustration, one of the nurses asked her, "Why do you keep doing things like this, anyway?"

Mandy couldn't see anything wrong with her reason for dowsing the woman. Why couldn't they see things as she did? There was no point even in trying to answer the nurse's question.

Another nurse, carrying something, entered the room. Two of the nurses came toward Mandy now, sending waves of fear through her. They became large, growing white objects in her vision. Then she saw the hypodermic needle, and her fear mounted. If she ran, if she tried to fight them off, she'd be locked up in that horrible room again, she knew. Wide-eyed and in terror, she tried to back up as the nurses clutched for her arms. Pinning her in the corner of the room, they held her as the third nurse rolled up Mandy's sleeve, rubbed her arm with alcohol and eased the needle into a vein. All she could do was scream, "No! God! Please help me!"

The nurses held their grip for a few moments and then gently eased her over onto the bed, and within minutes Mandy was asleep for the rest of the day.

For almost a week she shifted in and out of reality, barely able to distinguish what was real from what was a dream. She was tired of being so enervated, so listless, tired of dragging herself up and down the corridors in a meaningless parade from washroom to dining room to lounge and back to her own room. She silently prayed that God would free her from all of this; there must be some way. Any way. This wasn't living.

Gradually her head began to clear. It became easier to wake in the morning without a heavy head. How she hated that drugged feeling when her head felt literally too weighed down to hold up straight. There was such tension in the back of her neck that she found it hard to straighten up and focus properly. It took two more weeks for Mandy to start feeling her old self again. But what did that feel like, anyway? It had been so long since Mandy knew who she really was. Well, she'd rediscover who she was eventually; it was enough to know that the hospital staff considered her well on the road to recovery, even moving her to another ward, one with substantially more freedom of movement and activity.

When she first started feeling her head clear, she began to realize that the fastest way out of the hospital was to do as she was told, conform to the rules, get lots of rest and busy herself productively as much as possible. Her mother had brought in a few books, but she still didn't have the attention span to read them. But she did find a friend in a nurse who had charge of the occupational therapy room and who let her join a rug-hooking class. She hadn't realized how incredibly stifling, both physically and emotionally, the other ward was. It felt so good to be even a little more active now.

Seeing Mandy's progress, the medical staff allowed her more privileges, such as attending the relaxation class. How ironic, she mused. Here we aren't allowed so much as to go outside for a jog or even a short walk, and yet we're taking a class in relaxation. What these people need is real activity—physical exercise! She began to crave more physical activity and in private started her own rigorous program of calisthenics.

On a crisp, bright morning in early April, Doctor Bertinelli called Mandy into his office. He lifted his bulk from behind his desk as Mandy entered, a smile covering his large, round face.

"Good morning, Mandy. Have a seat."

He gestured to one of the chairs beside the desk and walked to the other, to sit beside her. A good psychiatrist, he knew that his desk represented a huge psychological barrier that separated his authoritarian institution—indeed, the whole of society—from the powerless patients in his care. He smiled again as he settled himself into the chair.

"We're really pleased with your progress, you know," he said.

"I'm grateful for that," said Mandy carefully, hoping that this wasn't a preface to discussion of some new problem.

"Yes, I'm especially happy to see that you're responding so well to the new medication. How do you feel this morning, anyway?"

"I feel fine. Better than I have in a long time."

She was cautious, not wanting to say anything 'strange.'

"Well, it's been nine weeks that you've been here in the hospital, and I thought you'd like to know we think you can be home for Easter. How would you like that?"

"Oh, Doctor Bertinelli," Mandy squealed, trying unsuccessfully to remain calm, "Do you really think so?" She brought her hands to her cheeks and had to fight back tears of happiness.

"That's wonderful, just wonderful," she said, thrilled at the thought of going home.

Easter was less than two weeks away.

Chapter Sixteen

"Are you all right now, Mommy?" Stephanie asked in the car, a concerned look on her face. "I hope you're not sick any more."

Mandy leaned over to hug her little girl even more tightly.

"Mommy's never felt better, sweetheart," she said.

Never, in fact, had she wanted to be away from anywhere quite so much, and never had she wished so fervently to be going home. And now she was almost there. The car turned onto Century Crescent.

When Mandy finally walked through the door with Alan, Anne and the children, she could hardly believe she was home. In the car Anne had had to keep the children from hanging all over their mother. Neither child had seen Mandy at any time during her nine-week confinement. Everyone thought it best that they stay away from the hospital, in case they might see something traumatic for them. With their grandmother attending every whim, however, they rarely missed their mother, even on Stephanie's birthday in February. She had had her fifth birthday at home with a few neighborhood friends, her father and grandmother. Her mother could only call home that day and wish her child a happy birthday and send her love over the phone.

But now she was home, and now she would assume fully the role she missed so much. Besides looking after the kids, there were so many things she wanted to do, simple little things like eating a crisp salad or devouring something very chocolate and very sweet.

She craved physical activity after being forced for so long to be sedentary. Tennis! I must take up tennis again, she decided. Decisions—those too! Decisions should be hers for a change. For those nine weeks Mandy had been treated as a child, or worse, as a lunatic incapable of doing anything rational, someone to be watched every moment for fear of doing something destructive. She had been allowed virtually no responsibility for her actions, and now she needed to prove to everyone that she could handle her life and those of her loved ones who depended on her.

As a result of these unspoken concerns, Mandy was considerably appalled when she learned that Alan had hired a woman to help look after the children until after dinner every day. What was the need? Mandy believed she could manage without the help of a complete stranger. If her mother wanted to stay another two weeks, that was fine; she even appreciated Anne's presence and loving care. But a nanny! If anyone besides Anne was going to care for the children, it would be their own mother.

Alan was insistent, however. He argued that even though Mandy might feel fine, the hospital environment was a highly protective one, and he didn't want any undue stress to intrude on their lives during this critical stage of readjustment to normal life. He understood exactly how Mandy felt, but just to make sure the transition was smooth, she should allow Gail, the nanny, to help around the house and with the children for a little while. What could it hurt? When the time was right, in just a short time, he would let Gail go and everything would be back to normal. Gail Smythe would start in less than two weeks, on the day that Anne was to return to Falmouth.

Mandy had to admit that everyone's life—not just her own—had been under serious strain over the past weeks. She sensed that Alan and Anne had endured the greatest stress, with Anne's being away from her own home and having to put up with Alan's evident distaste for her being in his house. Mandy knew quite clearly that Alan was constantly annoyed with Anne's continual babying of the children, always catering, he thought, to their every whim, having to entertain them at every turn, "spoiling them rotten," he claimed. How could he compete with Anne for his children's love and attention, especially if he had to work all day and often half the night while she was at his home ruining the children? Though Anne and Alan tried to remain outwardly friendly and courteous to one another, there was no question of the tension between them.

That first day at home was difficult for everyone, even though Anne knew something of manic-depression. Ruefully, Anne wondered why the hospital staff—especially Doctor Bertinelli—hadn't given someone in the family a list of do's and don'ts, or even the smallest instruction on where to go from here. Except for asking that

Mandy visit him once every two months, the doctor hadn't provided anything helpful for the family. There was one thing. A nurse had mentioned to Mandy something about a self-help group for manic-depressives that met regularly in Toronto. But how would that help Mandy or the family today, right now?

Because neither Anne nor Alan knew what to expect from Mandy, they decided that the best plan was to let her relax as she wanted, but more importantly, that she shouldn't become upset about anything. Even more critical than that, they believed, was to avoid any talk at all about the hospital or her condition. And to make sure there would be no unforeseen difficulties, they seemed to be going constantly from place to place, Alan's checking the children's behavior, Anne making sure of the condition of each room, everyone watching for anything that might create a problem. Mandy could sense the stiffness. To her they seemed to be walking on eggshells to avoid anything to disturb her. Quite obviously they were pampering her—but secretly it felt good to Mandy even though she felt guilty about it as well.

Wanting no special treatment and, also, to demonstrate that she was capable of doing things herself, Mandy tried to jump right in and help out. But Anne had already prepared lunch and the house was perfectly clean, so there was little to do but unpack. After lunch, when she tried to do the dishes her mother said she could manage just fine. Alan quickly grabbed a dishtowel and began wiping plates, insisting that Mandy take a break and watch the noon news or something. So she went to sit with the children, who were all over her, vying for attention, wanting to know what it was like in the hospital. When Stephen wiggled in under her mother's arm to get closer, Stephanie pouted and went running to her grandmother to complain, but received a stern warning not to bother her mother any more today.

By four in the afternoon Mandy knew she needed a nap. She hadn't really appreciated how tirelessly busy Stephen was becoming. In the "terrible twos" now, he seemed to be in motion all the time, an unceasing little bundle of energy. Mandy sensed a touch of panic rise in her stomach as she wondered, briefly, how she would manage without her mother there. In her own bed again—how wonderful it felt!—and the children corraled in the family room with grandmother, she felt troubled, guilty, for excusing herself for a nap, but in a short time she fell into a deep and restful sleep.

She awoke in the darkened room to Alan's gentle kiss. How nice that was, she thought, instantly feeling love for her man. He had had a late meeting and just arrived home. Anne had noticed that he seemed to be doing more of that these days, but as usual, she'd kept the thought to herself, not wanting to interfere.

"I think you've slept through dinner," said Alan gently.

"Mmm, I guess I have," Mandy said, stretching her arms upward.

"Don't worry," he said. "Your mother has something in the oven for you whenever you want it."

"That's okay. I'm not even hungry," she replied, finishing her stretch and reaching up to his neck to pull him down. They kissed again and nestled together on the bed.

"I have to catch up on all the hugging I've missed," said Mandy.

"Me too."

"I'm so happy to be home now," she said. "I want to hear everything about everything."

And for once Alan was eager to tell her what was going on at work, with local neighborhood gossip, little things he'd done around the house, and stories about the children over the past week or so. He was pleased to see her looking well rested—and so responsive tonight.

The last two months had been rather rough at work. It had been a hard decision to make, giving up a move and a promotion. The firm was very understanding about his decision to stay, that his wife's health came first. But Alan had kept her real problem from anyone, explaining simply that she'd had a nervous breakdown. In his view no one needed to know the truth. Nevertheless, he knew that the firm would think twice about sending him anywhere again. Mandy could sense a sadness—was it resentment?—in him as he spoke about his work. And it seemed that he'd withdrawn a little since she arrived home. Or was it only her imagination?

Perhaps it was just that her mother had been there for so long a time. For his part, Alan was quite unhappy knowing his plans had gone awry, and now he was undecided about his career goals at this point. He did know, on the other hand, that he was very happy about his in-laws going back to Falmouth. His home had been invaded for long enough.

Ralph had arrived from the Cape that afternoon, taking a taxi from the airport. Complaining as usual about the traffic and the long lines at the airport, nevertheless he confessed that he was happy to be in Toronto for the holiday. They would celebrate Easter together as a family, and try to forget the past ordeal of more than two months.

With the children tucked in bed, together in the family room the adults exchanged pleasant conversation over coffee. Mandy and her mother made an inventory of the food they needed for Easter weekend, while Alan and Ralph weighed the relative merits of the Boston Red Sox and the Detroit Tigers for the upcoming season. Mandy couldn't keep away from the dish of jellybeans; even she noticed her inordinate attraction to sweets since she got home.

Later, in the bedroom, Mandy slipped a pink satin nighty over her head. As it slid over her hips she noticed it didn't fall as loosely as before. Was she gaining weight again? Alan came out of the washroom and switched off the lights, and they both crawled under the covers.

"It's good to have you home," he said.

She reached over and slowly rubbed his chest.

"I missed you so much, Alan. I want to make this whole thing up to you."

She nestled closer.

Hesitantly Alan asked, "Are we supposed to be getting so, uh, serious, Mandy? Remember, you just got out of the hospital."

"Oh, I'm fine, and besides, the doctor didn't tell me that making love was bad for me, or for us, for that matter."

Alan sensed an urgency about Mandy's gestures as they touched each other's body. On the other hand, he felt reserved—not that he wasn't aroused physically, but because he knew that his feelings toward his wife weren't as they should be. Something was missing, though he wasn't sure just what it was. Time would have to tell.

But Mandy wanted to be touched, to be close to Alan, to be affirmed as a woman who was loved. She didn't know how to express

180

herself to him in any other way but to try to seduce him. But part of her didn't want to have to. She needed the reassurance of his wanting her totally, and he just didn't seem to care. His kisses, his movements were clearly more mechanical than ever before, and Mandy sensed it. Pretending to herself that it didn't matter, she moved her hips against his until, with some satisfaction, she felt his warmth flowing within her. For his benefit she uttered a little sigh of contentment and relief, but within minutes of their uncoupling, she rolled over in silence and curled up facing the wall, feeling dejected, unfulfilled.

Alan had already left for work by the time Mandy woke. Would she ever be ready to get up bright and early and swing into her old household routine? She had to start today. Again with a sense of urgency she breezed into the kitchen where Anne was already serving Ralph breakfast. Deciding therefore simply to have coffee, she sat with her father.

He said, "Good Friday's supposed to be a holiday in Canada, isn't it? Why did he have to leave for work? And so early?"

The realization caught Mandy by surprise.

"Oh well, he's so conscientious and he's trying hard to get ahead because he couldn't go to Vancouver, probably," she rationalized.

Ralph snorted derisively and shook open the newspaper.

Within herself Mandy began to ask why so much about Alan was left unsaid, why there was so little communication between them. So often she hadn't a clue what was going on in his mind. She must insist that they try to really communicate more.

"Let's get the dishes done and take the children for a walk, Mom, I feel so fat and lazy."

"Are you sure you want to do that, dear? Let me just finish up here, then maybe we can relax with the kids, play a game or something."

"But Mom, I need to do things around here. I need more exercise. There was just so little activity in the hospital. I really need some fresh air, and it looks like such a nice day out there. Let's go for a walk."

The children, who'd been watching television in the family room, heard part of the discussion and rushed into the kitchen, squealing with delight. Anne had to concede.

"All right, dear. Come help me put the dishes away then."

Ralph thought he'd stay behind and read the paper.

Coats on, Anne, Mandy and the children left for the park. Turning into the walkway that led to the little park behind the houses, the children ran ahead to try to find squirrels or a rabbit. Out of their hearing, Mandy suddenly asked, "Are you ashamed of me, Mom?"

"Of course not, dear," Anne replied. "Why do you ask that? Of course I'm not ashamed of you. Why should I be?"

"I'm still so confused, Mom. What's manic-depressive illness, anyway? Am I really crazy?"

"Do you really think the doctors would let you come home if you were? Of course you're not crazy, sweetheart. You're all better now."

"But sometimes I just don't feel like I belong here—or anywhere. I think I feel too many things sometimes, like I sense too much or something. I don't know."

"Mandy, honey, maybe you're just trying too hard now. It'll take some time to get used to everything again. You've had such a terrible shock to your system, you know."

Anne went on to explain what she had found out about the illness. She said she'd send her any more information that she could find once she got home and checked around. Certainly Murray Harding could send some material to her. While Mandy was still in the hospital Anne had bought a book, *From Sad to Glad*, which Doctor Bertinelli had recommended, but Mandy had had difficulty concentrating. Perhaps she should try now to read it. One of the few things Mandy retained from her earlier attempts at reading was that her illness involved some kind of biochemical problem, an imbalance in the brain, and now she wanted to learn more about it. This thing wasn't going to get the best of her. She was determined to fight it, to try harder than ever to be well and happy.

The children raced back, all out of breath, from playing among the trees. Hand in hand the foursome headed back to the house.

"Let me drive you to the store today, Mom," Mandy said quickly. "I've got to practise, and I ought to feel comfortable before you and Dad take off on Monday. The medication shouldn't be

182

affecting my vision and judgment any more; it's been a month now on this one."

"I don't want to disappoint you, dear, but the stores are closed."

"Oh shit, that's right. Rats."

"I wish you didn't have to use that word, dear."

"Sorry, Mom. Oh poop, then."

"Well, at least that's a little better," said Anne. "We can still take a drive if you're up to it."

After a pleasant drive with the children over to the Scarborough Bluffs and a walk along the lake shore, Mandy circled around and returned home by the downtown route, along Yonge Street, uncharacteristically light of traffic. Home again by three in the afternoon, after an hour of watching the children play in the family room and kitchen, Mandy started to feel very sleepy. The constant attention to the children's needs seemed to affect her adversely. She seemed constantly to be picking up toys or settling fights, and Stephanie's incessant chatter was giving her a headache. After the relative calm of the hospital, the perpetual noise and occasional rowdiness of the children at home seemed disproportionately exaggerated, irritating. Mandy began to feel very uneasy. Sensing her uneasiness and its cause, she began to doubt her ability to be a good mother, even to cope with day-to-day matters. She suddenly burst into tears and threw the dust rag down.

"It's all hopeless! I'm a failure! Shit!" she exclaimed to her shocked parents.

She turned and ran up to her room and flung herself across the bed, in tears. Anne came behind her and tried to reassure her.

"This is a natural reaction, dear. I think you're just trying to do too much."

"I don't see any big deal about that," Mandy said bitterly. "I'm not working hard. I just don't know if I can cope, Mom."

In growing fear she realized she was still mentally ill, though she was loathe to admit it even to herself. She hated the thought of it, hated how she felt. Her skin almost crawled. There was a constriction in her head, a pain at her forehead, and she rubbed it wishing she could somehow make it go away, or maybe that she could just disappear.

Everything in her world looked black.

Paradoxically, when Alan came home later with an Easter lily for her, all smiles, she only felt worse.

Alan, of course, was unaware of what had gone on during the day. He was genuinely happy to be home after a long week and he felt good that everything appeared to be getting better; that is, until he entered the bedroom and sensed the chill in the room. Anne had warned him that it hadn't been a very good day. Mandy was curled up in bed. She saw Alan standing with the plant in hand, and inexplicably she burst out crying. At the same time she thought to herself that here he was trying to be nice, and she was acting like such a jerk. What was wrong with her anyway? Why couldn't she just pull herself together?

He leaned down to kiss her, but he knew she wasn't responding. Quietly and solemnly, unwilling to deal with pessimism this evening, he changed clothes and went downstairs. Deciding to skip dinner she remained in bed, but was able to hear snatches of the conversation over dinner. Everyone was trying to be so polite. She grew more and more resentful as she lay there. Sure, the kids were all happy now and well fed, and now dad was home to play with them. Her mind withdrew inside itself as if something were calling or beckoning to her, trying to control her. What were these feelings of being controlled? Why couldn't she get rid of them?

She thought back to all the things she still remembered of her time in the hospital, of what she'd done—standing naked in the hallway, pouring water over that poor woman, the horrible feeling of being strapped down in that awful room with the peep hole, seeing strange messages. She really had done those things, she knew, and she had felt strongly from time to time that she was being protected. Was it God talking to her? Was she really someone special? How could she be if she couldn't even get through the day simply caring for her own children. Yet she loved this world so much. And despite her worry she felt peace—coming from somewhere; from inside?—that told her things would be all right. She loved Alan and the children. Her parents had been so good to her. Yet somehow she didn't belong here. She'd been able to see and feel things that normal people hadn't, and so she felt set apart. Perhaps now she could never again be anything but sick in her own eyes. But deep down she didn't feel crazy, just very tired and confused. Oh, how she needed to find someone else who had gone through this, to talk to someone. Was she the only one?

The family thought it best to leave Mandy alone that night. No one really knew for sure what to do, but if she wanted to be alone, perhaps that was best. They had to play out each scene by trial and error, not knowing what the consequences might be. And each of them was frightened in varying degree but unwilling to admit it. After all, no one else in either family had ever experienced anything like this before.

Mandy felt like an outsider by the time Alan came to bed that night. She lay there with her eyes open, staring at the ceiling or watching him silently as he got ready for bed. Alan was unnerved, knowing she was watching him coolly. Perhaps if he could just relax her a bit, as in the previous night. Under the covers he reached over to touch her, but Mandy stiffened. She turned toward the wall, and by her sigh he knew she was in no mood for being touched. He withdrew and rolled over, giving her a faint "Goodnight, Mandy. Hope you're feeling better tomorrow."

As she lay there in the darkness, she once again felt that she was driving him away. But he really didn't love her anyway, did he? Lying in the darkness, after a few minutes she suddenly became ashamed of how childishly she was acting. Turning toward her husband, she started to stroke his shoulder, to tell him how foolishly she'd been behaving, to apologize...

It was too late. He was already asleep. Or was he just pretending? She lay there, somehow cold inside, heaping more guilt upon herself until she finally fell asleep.

Alan wasn't in bed when she finally woke up. Her head felt so heavy, she could scarcely lift it off the pillow, and her mouth and lips were terribly dry. It was the medication; she hated how it seemed to dry her out. Thoughts seemed unclear to her until after she'd washed her face and brushed her teeth. She stared into the mirror but quickly looked away, not pleased with what she saw.

As she walked down to the kitchen Stephen ran to her and almost knocked her over with his enthusiasm. She tried to smile at him but knew it wasn't real. Something hurt too much.

Anne had looked after things as usual. The coffee was still hot but there was little evidence left of breakfast. Another pang of fear crept into Mandy's mind. What would she do after Tuesday, when her parents finally left for Falmouth?

"I love you, Mom," she said weakly. "I'll never be able to do things the way you do. I'm always failing, it seems."

Anne dropped her dishtowel on the countertop, walked over and gave her a hug.

"You just do things the way you do them, and don't worry about doing them my way. You'll do just fine."

They chatted at the table for a few minutes. Alan had taken Stephanie out for a walk to the store a little while ago, and Ralph was in the other room reading his paper. Mandy suddenly remembered that Easter was tomorrow.

"I'd really like to go to church, Mom. The whole family, I mean. Wouldn't that be nice?"

"That's a nice idea, dear. We can have a light breakfast and then have dinner when we get home. I'll put the ham on before we go. But do you suppose Alan would want to go?"

"I hope so. He's not much on church, but I'll tell him he has to, for the kids."

Mandy sipped her coffee then looked up again.

"Mom," she exclaimed, brightening, "let's go out and have our hair done. I just have to look nice tomorrow. Dad can watch Stephen for a little while, can't he?"

Grampa was unusually agreeable.

"You girls just set us up with something to keep us busy and the little tyke and I will be all right. Besides, Alan and Steffie will be back soon and I suppose there's some sports on TV. You go on and have a good time."

The ladies indeed had a pleasant time. After having their hair washed and set at Hair Today, in Willowdale Mall, they made a quick stop at a children's clothing store, where they bought new Easter outfits for the youngsters. It was some time after four p.m. that the women returned, in high spirits, to the house.

Looking up from the track meet, Alan saw with relief that

Mandy obviously felt and looked better than on the previous day. It was then that he realized that each day presented a different Mandy and that he never would quite know what to expect any more when he walked through the door.

That night, however, everyone seemed to be in a holiday mood. After Stephanie and Stephen went to bed, the adults even sat down to a friendly game of cards, Ralph and Alan with their scotch on the rocks, and the women sipping white wine. Mandy soon became giddy, an effect of her medication, and had trouble concentrating on the game. She knew after one drink that she'd had enough but said nothing.

Looking up over her cards and smiling, Mandy saw the others more relaxed than they'd appeared in a long while. They were laughing and talking as if nothing had happened to change their lives or their feelings toward one another. She was happy for them. Perhaps if she weren't here they would be really happy. What was her reason for being here anyway? She didn't make a very good mother or wife, and she certainly wasn't a good child to her parents.

A great sadness seemed to sweep through her. Suddenly she pushed back her chair and stood up.

"I'm really sorry," she said. "I'm really very tired, and I think I need to go to bed."

"Wouldn't you know it," Ralph said in feigned consternation. "Just when I'm beginning to get the hang of this game."

"You just go ahead, dear," said Anne. "We've had a big day anyway, and we all have to get an early start for tomorrow."

Mandy said, "I'll be all ready for church tomorrow. You're coming, aren't you, Alan?"

"Well, I don't know," said Alan, leaning back to sip his scotch. "Why don't you just go yourselves? I'm not sure I want to. Church is just full of a bunch of phonies who come out once or twice a year. They're all a bunch of hypocrites who put on their church coats on Sunday and take them off Monday."

Anne smiled. "It's easy to understand why you'd think that, but can you think of a better place for hypocrites to be on Easter Sunday morning than in church?"

"Oh Alan," Mandy pleaded, "It's Easter, and we should be

setting a good example for the kids. And it would be so nice for our whole family to be together. Just this once, please?"

"Well, hell's bells," he conceded, outnumbered. "I guess it wouldn't hurt."

Mandy leaned over and hugged his shoulders.

"Oh, it's going to be so nice. You'll see," she said, beaming. "Now I have to go to bed. Goodnight, everybody."

But as she mounted the stairs, she had a feeling of unsureness about what tomorrow would bring. She was supposed to do something, but what? By the time her footsteps reached the bathroom, she was certain that she would learn what it was in the church service. And perhaps she would learn who she really was. Was she to rise somehow? Was she going to die? Incomplete thoughts flew into her mind, flittingly, as she brushed her teeth and got ready for bed. How strange it felt, to try to pretend you were normal when you were receiving such messages, when such thoughts kept racing.

By the time she reached the bed, she was clearly unhappy with herself. She couldn't control the thoughts, keep them from bubbling up from within. Her mind raced, flew back to that horrible day in the abortionist's house. She'd killed her baby. She felt so wicked. Tears started to flow as she recalled every detail. Yes, she must surely be punished for what she'd done. Her body started feeling the pain again as she relived the experience. Her mind continued to race. So totally worthless, she thought. Out loud she uttered, "Oh, please God, forgive me. I'll do anything you ask."

As the words left her mouth she envisioned herself suspended on the cross. At that moment she knew God was there, somehow, with her. She could believe in Him, trust in Him, adore Him. Willingly she would submit to whatever it took to be loved by Him.

Feeling a great catharsis, cleansed to the bone—but very tired—she realized her whole body was soaked with perspiration. Wondering what God had in store, and ready to accept His will, she sat on the side of the bed, hoping that God would want her to disappear. With a deep breath she felt a deep calm envelop her body, as if God were speaking to her through her heart. She was forgiven; she had always been forgiven. Only she, herself, had condemned herself, over and over again. "Thank you, Father. Thank you so much," she whispered. Suddenly she remembered how she had pleaded for her life, once before, in the coma. "Thank you for my life," she added.

She actually could feel, in a warm, tingling sensation, that she was loved, that now, finally, she could begin to believe. Linda, her friend back at school, must have been trying to say this to her. Now she understood something of the deep peace that Linda must have had.

Mandy went to the dresser and pulled out a fresh nighty, changed, and washed her face. Back in bed she laid her head against the pillow and sighed, feeling calm, that everything would now be all right. Eyes closed and smiling, she fell into a deep and restful sleep, and when Alan came upstairs to bed, he only saw her peacefully sleeping with almost a smile on her face. He gazed at her by the light from the bathroom. If only it could be like this forever, he thought.

Chapter Seventeen

Mandy was the first one awake on Easter morning, even before the children started to stir. Oh good, she thought to herself a bit mischievously. Quietly but quickly she slipped out of bed and hurried downstairs to prepare a surprise for everyone. She was going to show them she could take control again. Easter had always been her favorite holiday—as well as Hallowe'en—partly because she could be as much of a child as the children. An early morning Easter egg hunt was traditional for the family, and there would be one today. Finding the bag of Easter candies that she and Anne had bought, she set about hiding them all over the living and dining rooms. Then she set the table for a festive breakfast, placing the two Easter baskets by the children's places at the table. She was making the batter for pancakes when she heard the children stirring upstairs.

Anne was so surprised to smell the aroma of coffee drifting into her room that she put on her robe and pattered into the kitchen to see what was going on. Mandy's smiling face greeted her.

"Happy Easter, Mom. I love you so much."

Mandy hugged her mother strongly, and Anne was a bit overtaken with the surprise.

"Would you look at this!" she said.

"I wanted to surprise you and give you a treat because you've done so much for me."

They shared another close hug, and then Stephen bounded into the kitchen. He ran to the women and lunged into them, grasping their legs, joining in with the hug.

Within twenty minutes the whole family was up and full of the excitement of the morning that Mandy had created with her Easter surprise. This was like the old Mandy, the vivacious, happy girl that everyone remembered. The children were wild with excitement as they scurried around the living room and dining area looking for treats to fill their already overflowing baskets. Mandy beamed with pride for getting the elaborate breakfast ready. Alan smiled at her from across the table. He was going to enjoy today; even having to go to church seemed much easier to handle.

The family made a handsome sight as they walked up the aisle to take a pew that was closer to the front than they'd intended. The church was packed. Mandy thought she would burst with the joy that filled her. There was so much to be thankful for, and she was full of love for everyone there. Glancing down the pew at her family, she knew she had to be the luckiest woman alive. And she was particularly happy to have a wonderful secret inside, the knowledge that God loved her and that she was forgiven. This was an extra special service for Mandy. Her voice rang out with joy as they sang the last hymn, and no one noticed or cared about those eyes that glistened with tears of happiness as they left the church.

On this clear morning the sun shone brightly and the whole world seemed to be celebrating the birth of spring. The Marsdens had a wonderful Easter dinner. The pain and doubt of the past had seemed to vanish. It wasn't until the family started getting ready for bed that evening that a sense of quiet intruded, as everyone thought that tomorrow would be the last day for Anne and Ralph. They would be packing up to go home. But in the afternoon Gail Smythe, who would be helping with the house and the children, was scheduled to arrive.

This was going to be a big adjustment for everyone. For Mandy, the hardest thing to accept was that her mother and father were leaving, and now she would have to stand on her own two feet again. But she believed she could do it. There was no choice; she'd have to.

The morning of departure was painful, as usual, for everyone. Both women were trying their best not to cry as the men carried the bags out to the car. Anne, concerned that Mandy wasn't strong enough yet to manage on her own, tried to convey confidence as she hugged her loved ones. Ralph kissed Mandy and shook hands with Alan, but said nothing for fear of saying something wrong. More than anything, the Cartwrights wanted their daughter's happiness. Alan simply wanted the goodbyes done with so he could go to the office and get on with his life, in peace. Finally, amid forced smiles and well wishes, Anne and Ralph got into the taxi and, waving, drove off.

Mandy's tears glistened as she felt for an instant that she was still a frightened little girl—until she grasped the hands of her children and walked back into the house with Alan.

Mrs. Smythe turned out to be very helpful and efficient—perhaps too much so. Fiftyish, businesslike and precise, she had perfected what she considered a logical method of cleaning, a reflection of her life-view, that life should be approached rationally, determinedly, with a stiff upper lip. This approach to life and work, of course, countered that of Mandy, but Alan sensed a kindred soul in Gail Smythe. Increasingly uncomfortable with her, Mandy began to feel inadequate about her own capabilities. Mrs. Smythe always seemed to do everything more efficiently. And she had a system she didn't want changed.

At times Mandy felt like a prisoner in her own home. She had to admit that the children were happy that she could spend so much time with them, since Mrs. Smythe took charge of everything else. But Mandy's confidence and her sense of independence weakened progressively, and she felt intimidated by the woman, unable to speak up to her. After a few weeks she marshaled her courage and voiced her concern to Alan once Mrs. Smythe had gone home for the evening.

"I don't think I want to have Mrs. Smythe here any more," Mandy said. "My medication's keeping me under control and I really think I can handle things on my own."

"What are you saying?" he shot back. "Things are going smoothly, aren't they? I never seem to know where you're coming from these days. I think we ought to keep her for a while."

Here it was again, he thought. Once everything finally seems to be going along just fine, she throws a wrench into the works. Was there nothing he could do right? Why, shit, it didn't seem worth the effort any more. Life was so much freer and easier at work. Everything at home was a strain or some kind of problem. What the hell was wrong with this woman?

"Maybe you should think about a part-time job or something to occupy your time," he offered, trying to control his anger. "Maybe you should get out of the house more often. I'm sure you'd feel better."

"I don't want a job," Mandy retorted. "I would just like to have a little control over my life, over something again."

"Well Goddammit, I'm trying the best I can," countered Alan. "Give me a fucking break, will you?"

In his view Alan was doing his best to provide a good home for his wife and children, even to hiring a full-time woman to help out, just so Mandy could be free to do what she wanted. But that was the trouble—Mandy didn't know what she wanted. Nor did she ever know. Being a good wife and mother was all she thought she'd like to be. But now she wanted desperately to stand on her own two feet, and she didn't like being watched or criticized by such a perfect housekeeper.

Eventually Mandy acquiesced on the subject of Gail Smythe. Life at home was easier, she had to admit, if more frustrating. And she could in fact spend more time with the children during the day. If only she could keep from dwelling on what she believed was Mrs. Smythe's silent condemnation of her.

Mandy's love for Alan and the children finally made her brave enough to step outside her cocoon-like environment. One Saturday, deciding to leave Gail to her own devices at the house, she took Stephanie and Stephen to the library, to enroll them in a program for young children. There she noticed an announcement for a night course on personal growth, "Know Thyself and Be Free," which looked interesting. Yes, she thought, that's what she wanted to be.

To her delight the course was a breath of fresh air. Eight women attended, all young mothers like herself, and the teacher was a very gentle woman, with an East Indian background, Mandy suspected. Every word she spoke seemed to flow from her mouth so smoothly and softly exact. The class would engage in a form of therapy exercise to try to touch their true selves. If anything, the class was new and interesting to Mandy, who was thoroughly delighted with the experience of learning again. After a few weeks her excitement began to spread into her home life, and Alan once again saw Mandy happier with herself, something he desperately wanted for her.

In the fourth week of class, however, Mandy experienced an event that frightened her. Like the others, she was relaxed in the dimly lit room, attempting to get in touch with her subconscious. A large candle flickered on a low table in the center of the room. Everyone was relaxed in the candlelight, breathing deeply, becoming more and more introspective, more relaxed. In a soft, mesmerizing voice the teacher described serene pictures, helping them to touch their subconscious.

Through the light Mandy eventually began to see a beautiful clear crystal emerging through a cloudy mist. It seemed tall and jagged, with thousands of facets that glistened brightly as the light hit its surface. She felt a marvelous warmth envelop her body and then a wonderful tingling sensation inside, and she began to cry softly. As she did, she was consumed in a huge ball of light, producing a tremendous feeling of strength and power and warmth that engulfed her. Believing this was something from God, she sat marveling, quietly weeping tears of joy and peace, knowing she was truly loved. The crystal was a beautiful creation of God that could reflect His light through its many facets. For the first time in her life she felt that her intense feelings were all right to experience, to share with others. She was free to be herself at last!

In the sharing time later, it became obvious that the other participants had also experienced wonderful visual pictures. Everyone went home feeling special that night.

Mandy, in particular, found herself with a strongly renewed interest in spiritual things. Ever since Stephanie's birth—since the trauma that developed from the hypnosis—she had stifled such things. But now this, this vision or whatever it was... She determined to be more sensitive to matters of the spirit, to learning more about herself, and therefore resolved to read everything the teacher recommended.

But she knew her nerves needed more relaxation and so decided to enroll in a yoga class. Uncomfortable with the Eastern philosophy subtly expounded by the teacher, nonetheless through the exercises she developed a controlled peace and calm from learning to breathe properly again. It was as if her body were trying to heal itself. She remembered how wonderfully relaxed she had felt with the breathing exercises that she had been introduced to during her early experimentations with self-hypnosis, and that her body seemed to like it. This time, however, she would be more in tune with her body's responses. She would concentrate on her total reactions.

Doctor Bertinelli was quite pleased with Mandy's apparently steady progress. The anti-depressant medication she regularly took obviously stabilized her condition quite well, and the renewed outlook certainly helped her overall state. But she was unhappy with a slight weight gain, for which the doctor simply prescribed more exercise and a careful diet. Mandy soon became tired of the routine fifteen-minute hospital checkups and—more importantly—the lack of answers from Doctor Bertinelli to most of her questions.

At a health food store one day, following a visit to the psychiatrist, Mandy happened across an announcement for a meeting of the Toronto manic-depressive self-help group. This must be the one the nurse mentioned, she thought. Surreptitiously removing it from the bulletin board, she folded it and carried it home for Alan to see. She almost had to beg him to accompany her, but he reluctantly agreed, sensing shades of the earlier problems with hypnosis and the first childbirth.

The evening of the meeting was uncomfortably warm and muggy for early summer. Pulling into the church parking lot, Alan sat bolt upright on seeing the number of cars already in the lot.

"Must be something else happening too," he offered.

"Probably so."

"Well, we probably won't have any trouble spotting where the loonies are," Alan said, turning the car into a vacant spot. Mandy shot him an acid look.

Inside, surprisingly, some 200 people crowded the church for the meeting, even with the humid conditions. Taking a seat near the back, they sat and looked around at the audience. Mandy dug her elbow into Alan's arm. "These people look just as normal as you," she whispered. Alan nodded, peering toward the platform.

The main speaker, a psychiatrist from The Clarke Institute in Toronto, told the audience all there was to know about the self-help group and relations of the group to the Institute, and then spoke of recent developments in the treatment of manic-depressive illness, concentrating on advances in the use of lithium, followed by a short question-and-answer session. Afterward, there was a time for informal conversation and refreshments, but when the questions ended and the audience started moving from the pews to the church hall in the basement, Mandy turned to Alan. "We can go home if you want. I don't need to go downstairs, and we should get home to the kids."

Alan needed no further prompting.

In reality, Mandy was quite disturbed with the doctor's talk about lithium and his approach to treating manic depression. That chemical had caused her nothing but problems, and she had had enough experience with numbing and mind-altering medications. She wanted to become well and whole!

By midsummer she was feeling alive and energetic, but to Alan she was becoming almost a health fanatic, with her vegetarian salads, herbal teas and other exotic foods. Mrs. Smythe and Alan were becoming annoyed, as well, at the pungent smell of burning incense. They had to admit, on the other hand, that Mandy's moods were definitely leveling out; she was changing, mostly for the good. She had decided to let her hair grow out again, and not to perm it any more. She began to wear very casual clothes—long, flowing peasant skirts and comfortable blouses. Alan said little about her change of appearance, but at times he felt quite uncomfortable with Mandy's new identity.

A serious crisis developed at a fashionable weekend barbecue party thrown by a prospective company client at his spacious home in Oakville, Ontario, a posh suburban community not far from Toronto. At that time Mandy was particularly happy about herself because she had lost ten pounds on her new diet and felt like a teenager, full of life and fun and ready for a good time. Alan, of course, was concerned about making a good impression for his client. After all, this was the first time since Mandy had been hospitalized that she had been invited to a gathering of company brass.

It was an elegant lawn party outside by the pool, adjacent to the sprawling, ranch-style house. The invited guests—the men dressed in light suits and ties, and the women in expensive, flowing dresses and some wearing broad-brimmed summer hats—stood around in small groups of three or four, chatting casually, admiring the ambience. A butler and a maid brought champagne and hors d'oeuvres on silver trays, and Mandy was glowing by the time she started sipping her second glass. She was pleasantly surprised to see that she was the youngest and prettiest at the affair.

Soon bored by the total absence of activity, she went to stand by the side of a small fountain that splashed merrily into the shallow end of the pool. Staring at the bubbling water, suddenly she felt impish and flirty, and giggled out loud for feeling as she did. No one seemed to notice.

As the afternoon wore on she found less and less in common with the others there. The men were off in groups, deep in conversations about work. All the wives seemed to chat meaninglessly about clothes or restaurants or their plans for summer trips. Once she tried to interject a bit of humor into a conversation among the ladies, but no one seemed to get the joke. Excusing herself after a few moments, she went to help herself to a vodka collins at the bar. The bartender, young and handsome, seemed the only one there with any life in his eyes; Mandy gave him a wink, smiled, and tripped off with her drink, leaving the bartender baffled and curious.

Walking around the edge of the pool and into a beautifully landscaped section a short distance from the main gathering, she spotted a distinguished, older gentleman sitting on a settee, alone, and walked over to join him.

"Hello," she said. "I'm Mandy Marsden. Would you mind if I kept you company for a little while?"

"Not at all. Pardon me if I don't get up."

He gestured toward his ankles, then reached toward Mandy to shake her hand. "Acton Mansfield's the name. My feet hurt a bit; must be getting old."

Mandy saw in his face only sadness and tension.

"I know a great thing for your feet," she said enthusiastically. "Do you know, I've just finished taking a relaxation course that showed how to unstress the foot muscles."

She sat down beside Acton Mansfield and allowed her enthusiasm to get the best of her.

"Would you like a foot massage? You wouldn't believe how wonderful it makes you feel. All the stress and tension go right away."

Under the circumstances, Acton Mansfield couldn't refuse

graciously. She was so persuasive the man had to say yes, and before he knew it she was on her knees before him, his shoes on the ground, and she was gently massaging his foot.

"Oh boy," he said with evident pleasure. "That really does the trick. It feels better already."

He leaned his head back on the cushion and closed his eyes, feeling better than he had in weeks. Mandy smiled at him and continued kneading his sole with her thumbs.

At that moment Alan, who had become curious at Mandy's absence from the main group, rounded the corner and spotted them, Mandy on her knees with his client's father, Acton Mansfield, sprawled out before her on the settee. One of the firm's senior partners, Reynold Levine, his wife and two friends also happened to notice Mandy on the ground, in what appeared, for all the world—at least from their angle—to be Mandy in a compromising position with Mr. Mansfield. Levine couldn't help but laugh out loud.

Alan realized that others now saw Mandy's bizarre behavior and, terribly embarrassed, quickly apologized to Levine for her outlandish stunt. Striding stiffly and quickly over to Mandy, he lifted her to her feet and whisked her away to a corner, his look of disgust all too clear to Mandy. He was furious.

"Just what the fuck are you trying to do to me?" he demanded, trying his best to control his voice.

Instantly Mandy burst into tears, covering her face with her hands.

"Now just what the hell were you doing with that guy, trying to give him a blow job or something?"

Mandy was shocked. She looked up squarely into his face.

"I didn't see anything wrong in what I was doing," she replied innocently. "I was just rubbing his foot. It was hurting him. What's wrong with that? He enjoyed it, and it was making him feel better. What's so bad about that?"

Frustrated with his wife and still enraged, Alan could only scowl terribly at her, unable to find words.

"In fact, the more I think about it," she added, "the more I believe it was okay to do that."

She looked past him to the group that had gathered at the

corner of the pool to watch the proceedings, all the while pretending to be involved in their own conversations. She lifted her face in their direction and purposely raised her voice.

"All those stuffy old biddies need to do is to relax, loosen up and realize the joys of getting in touch with their bodies again."

"Keep your goddamn voice down," Alan demanded. "They'll hear you. Just shut the hell up, will you?"

Mandy became indignant. She didn't care if she created a scene. In fact, she wanted to.

"Fuck you!" she exclaimed, almost hoping everyone would hear her.

Suddenly having to show them all, she pulled away from him and ran to the change house beside the pool. Acton Mansfield's son William, whose house it was, had encouraged everyone to bring a swim suit, and here they were. But none of the women ever dared get her hair wet. So Mandy decided to show them what swimming really was. Hastily changing into her swimsuit, out of the change room she strolled, and right over to the side of the pool, where she dove in. Alan, trying to explain his wife's antics, had no chance to prevent her. For several minutes she swam around at the deep end, oblivious to anyone else. Finally she swam idly toward the shallow end, where she stood up, walked up the steps and into the change house, dried off and changed into her clothes.

That evening she and Alan rode home in chilled silence. Mandy was sure she never wanted to attend any of those stuffy affairs again. Alan had had enough. He was convinced he no longer wanted to be saddled with this immature woman who obviously needed help, who was destroying his life in the process. He was done with it. Worlds apart now, there was no use pretending any more. It was over.

Nevertheless, Alan didn't want to hurt Mandy. He just wanted to be free from the hassle that Mandy always seemed to create. All he ever wanted was a quiet home life and a successful career, to present himself and his family in a constructive, positive light. Mandy, who he knew was trying to be true to herself and her feelings, only thwarted him at every turn. And then there were the children. Alan loved them but knew he couldn't care for them alone. Could Mandy, for that matter?

The next few weeks were torture for both of them. The nights were chilly even though it was early August. They tried sleeping in the same bed for a while until they realized the distance between them, the silence and heartache, just kept them both awake, tossing and turning, either sleeping in a cold sweat or lying in tears. Often one of them would be startled awake if they did happen to fall asleep.

Mandy ached from the absence of physical touch. She wanted so much to reach out, to move her hand over to touch her husband's back as he lay with his body facing the wall. But she couldn't.

They had nothing more to say. Neither of them wanted this any more. Mandy believed she still loved Alan... Or was it just that she couldn't imagine what life would be like on her own? Was it all only a formality, was she really just craving security? A million and one doubts continued to torment her mind.

Some days later, on a Thursday, Alan arrived home in the middle of the afternoon, pleasantly surprising Mandy. She opened the front door for him and smiled.

"What a surprise this is," she said. "How come you're off early today?"

He eased past her and walked into the hallway.

"I just can't stay here any longer," he explained. "I think it's a good idea if we separate. I've seen a lawyer who's going to make things official. I just want you to know that I'll be very fair to you and the kids regarding the money."

The announcement numbed Mandy. She knew things were impossible the way they were, but she wasn't prepared for such finality. Immediately panicking, she began to cry uncontrollably. In the midst of her sobs she realized that Alan had purposely come home when Mrs. Smythe and Stephen would be away picking Stephanie up at school. He'd planned it this way. This was it. Really it.

The thought of the end terrified her.

"Alan," she pleaded, "please, you've got to think it over. There must be another way."

She grasped futilely at his neck, but he pulled away.

"I'll do anything you say," she begged. "You just can't leave me. Think of the kids. Please, Alan. Please!"

He held her away. Resolute, beyond persuasion, he went

upstairs and packed his clothes. He carried his suits and a few belongings out to the car while Mandy looked on speechlessly, in shock. When he was finished he handed her a slip of paper.

"This is my new address and my lawyer's name. You'd better get yourself a lawyer, but don't worry about it too much. I'll give you everything I can. I'll be back in a few days for the rest of my stuff."

Words escaping her, she stared blankly at him.

"Kiss the kids for me," he said. "I'm sorry, but I have to go. I've got a lot to do today."

Climbing into the car, he looked back at Mandy, tears in his eyes, wanting to say something but not finding words. He stared at his wife for a moment, briefly wondering why things couldn't have been different, then turned and drove off.

Still numb, unable to cry, she walked through the front door, leaving it open as she stumbled upstairs to their bedroom. She glanced around slowly and rested her eyes on the mirror above the dresser. Giving herself a long, critical look, she finally sighed deeply. To her reflection she said, "Well, lady, it's all up to you now."

EPILOGUE

This isn't the end. In a sense, Mandy's story is just beginning, for *A Body Innocent* covers only the events that led to illness. Mandy must now accept and learn to cope with the many physical and emotional effects of her illness in everyday life. And there are unresolved questions: Has Alan left for good? Will Mandy be able to withstand the pressures of single motherhood? Can she begin to unravel the mysteries of her confused and hurting mind?

The second book of *Feeling the Rainbow*, - *The Awakening* - explores these and other questions as we watch Mandy begin to mature and grow as a person, not just a mental patient. But her sanity is tested time and again as she encounters unexpected personal challenges, awakens to her sexuality, tries to re-enter the real world of working women, fights a sometimes cold insensitive legal system, and searches for strength to conquer her greatest fears.

The Awakening takes us closer to understanding that most elusive of quarry — the hurting human mind that has undergone stress and borne the consequences.

In the natural evolution of her search for wholeness, Mandy also discovers a desperate need to be renewed, to discern truth from untruth. Book three of *Feeling the Rainbow* thus takes us into murky waters — an exploration of the relationship between psychiatry and religion as part of Mandy's quest for sanity. She encounters many who profess to know "the truth," including gurus of the New Age. Through persistence, patience and faith, she comes to understand what will keep her "safe and sound" — with this knowledge becoming a glowing example for us all.